THE WOODWORKER'S
POCKET BOOK

C.H. Hayward

HarperCollins*Publishers*

First published in 1992 by HarperCollins*Publishers*, London

First published by Evans Brothers Ltd 1949
Revised and reset edition published by Bell and Hyman 1983

© HarperCollins*Publishers* 1987, 1992

ISBN 0 00 412891 5

Printed in Great Britain
by Cox & Wyman Ltd, Reading

Timber — how calculated

Imperial — Metric Measurements

From 1 April 1970 timber is to be sold in three main ways; per metre super or square metre; per metre run or lineal metre; and per cube or cubic metre.

The change-over will take some time to complete and it is quite likely that the old Imperial system will continue for some time. In anticipation of the change, however, we have followed metric sizes on the following pages. Where doubt exists we suggest that the reader turn to the conversion tables on page 125.

Per metre super. A metre super is a square metre and the wood can be of any proportions that will give this area. Thickness does not enter into the calculation. Thus a piece of wood 1 m. long by 1 m. wide is obviously 1 m. super; but equally so is a piece 2 m. long by 0·50 m. or 4 m. long by 0·25 m. To find the superficial area multiply the length by the width, both in metres. Thus a piece 3 m. long by 0·120 m. (that is 120 millimetres) is 0·360 m. super. If you are quoted at 22 p per m. super for a piece 2·5 m. long by 0·20 m. wide the calculation is:

$$2·5 \times 0·20 = 0·5 \text{ m. super}$$
$$0·5 \times 22 = 11 \text{ p}$$

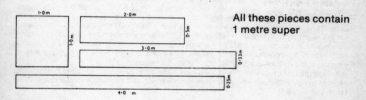

All these pieces contain 1 metre super

Per metre run. Here the only dimension concerned is length. Width and thickness are ignored. If 24 p per metre run is quoted for a piece 2·5 metres long, the price is 24 p × 2·5 = 60 p. Softwoods are generally sold on this basis and there is a growing tendency for certain hardwoods to be so sold, especially when in narrow strip form. Sometimes squares (that is timber square in section — 50 mm. by 50 mm. or 38 mm. by 38 mm. etc.) are sold by the metre run.

Per cube (metre). To the man not used to it this can be one of the most confusing methods. The cost per cube is the price of a solid block of timber 1 m. long, 1 m. wide, and 1 m. thick, or of any other shape which will give the same volume. You have, therefore, to find the cubic content of the timber you are buying before you can arrive at the cost per metre run.

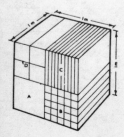

All these strips are 1 metre runs
In section they are:
A. 0·5 m. sq.
B. 0·1 m. sq.
C. 0·5 m. × 0·05 m.
D. 0·25 m. sq.

Timber — how calculated

Men in the trade use sets of tables so that the cost can be arrived at quickly, and we give one or two tables opposite which will help. It is as well, however, to understand how calculations are made. To find the cubic content of the timber you are buying, multiply the length by the width by the thickness all in metres. Thus, suppose the wood is 2·5 metres long by 0·19 m. wide by 0·020 m. thick. The calculation is:

$$2·5 \times 0·19 \times 0·020 = 0·0095 \text{ cubic metre}$$

If the wood is quoted at £12 per cube the cost is: £12 × 0·0095 = 11·4 p. To find the cost per metre run:

$$11·4 \div 2·5 \text{ (the length of the wood)} = 4·56 \text{ p}$$

A quick method of finding the cost per metre run when the price per cubic metre is given is to multiply the width of the wood in metres by the thickness in metres by the price in pence per cubic metre, giving the answer in pence. Thus to take the example given:

$$0·19 \times 0·020 \times 1200 = 4·56 \text{ p}$$

In the round. Timber in the log is usually sold 'per cubic metre'. If the log is a squared one (as in the case of imported mahogany) the cubic content is easily arrived at by multiplying length by width by thickness (all in metres). Thus, a log 4 m. by 0·6 m. by 0·6 m. contains 1·44 cubic metres. If the log is round there is a fairly simple way of arriving at the cube figure. First the girth is measured with a tape a little short of the centre, this allowing for the slight taper in length. A rule accepted from long experience is to regard this girth as equal to the combined sides of a squared log. Thus, assuming the girth to be 2 metres, each side of the corresponding square log would be 0·5 metre. If the log is, say, 5 metres long the cubic content is 5 × 0·5 × 0·5 = 1·25 cubic metres. See page 4.

An approximate rule like this applies only to felled logs, not to standing timber or to trees of irregular growth where wastage in conversion and allowance for bark have to be taken into account.

Softwood in future is to be imported in metric sizes, though stocks in imperial measurements are likely to last for some time. The range of new sizes is considerably smaller than hitherto, and is as in the following chart.

THICKNESS (mm.)	WIDTH (mm.)								
	75	100	125	150	175	200	225	250	300
16	x	x	x	x					
19	x	x	x	x					
22	x	x	x	x					
25	x	x	x	x	x	x	x	x	x
32	x	x	x	x	x	x	x	x	
38	x	x	x	x	x	x	x		
44	x	x	x	x	x	x	x	x	x
50	x	x	x	x	x	x	x	x	x
63		x	x	x	x	x	x		
75		x	x	x	x	x	x	x	x
100		x		x		x		x	x
150			x			x			x
200						x			
250								x	
300									x

Prices: £2 £3 £4 cu. ft = ×35·3147 for cost cu. m. at say £75, 100, 150/m.³

1" = 25·4 mm.

		Metric (mm.)	Cross sectional area m²	£ Price per 10 m. length		
	Imperial (in.)			£75/m.³	£100/m.³	£150/m.³
Squares	1 × 1	25 × 25	0·000625	0·47	0·63	0·94
	1½ × 1½	38 × 38	0·001444	1·08	1·44	2·17
	2 × 2	50 × 50	0·0025	1·88	2·50	3·75
	2½ × 2½	60 × 60	0·0036	2·70	3·60	5·40
	3 × 3	75 × 75	0·005625	4·22	5·63	8·44
	4 × 4	100 × 100	0·0100	7·50	10·00	15·00
	6 × 6	150 × 150	0·0225	16·88	22·50	33·75
Wood ½" thick	3	75	0·0009375	0·70	0·94	1·41
(12·5 mm.	4	100	0·00125	0·94	1·25	1·88
thick)	5	125	0·0015625	1·17	1·56	2·34
	6	150	0·001875	1·41	1·88	2·81
	7	180	0·00225	1·69	2·25	3·38
	8	200	0·0025	1·88	2·50	3·75
Wood ¾" thick	3	75	0·0015	1·13	1·50	2·25
(20 mm.)	4	100	0·0020	1·50	2·00	3·00
	5	125	0·0025	1·88	2·50	3·75
	6	150	0·0030	2·25	3·00	4·50
	7	180	0·0036	2·70	3·60	5·40
	8	200	0·0040	3·00	3·60	6·00
Wood 1" thick	3	75	0·001875	1·41	1·88	2·81
(25 mm.)	4	100	0·0025	1·88	2·50	3·75
	5	125	0·003125	2·34	3·13	4·68
	6	150	0·003750	2·82	3·75	5·63
	7	180	0·0045	3·38	4·50	6·75
	8	200	0·0050	3·75	5·00	7·50
Wood 1½" thick	3	75	0·0030	2·25	3·00	4·50
(40 mm.)	4	100	0·0040	3·00	4·00	6·00
	5	125	0·0050	3·75	5·00	7·50
	6	150	0·0060	4·50	6·00	9·00
	7	180	0·0072	5·40	7·20	10·80
	8	200	0·0080	6·00	8·00	12·00

Costs in £ per 10 m. length

Timber-how calculated

The following approximate equivalents, metric and imperial are given for quick reference.

mm.	16	19	22	25	32	38	44	50	63
in.	$\frac{5}{8}$	$\frac{3}{4}$	$\frac{7}{8}$	1	$1\frac{1}{4}$	$1\frac{1}{2}$	$1\frac{3}{4}$	2	$2\frac{1}{2}$
mm.	75	100	125	150	175	200	225	250	300
in.	3	4	5	6	7	8	9	10	12

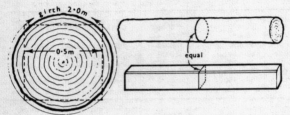

Calculating content in the round

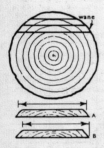

The wane. When planks are cut from the round log it is customary to allow for the "wane" edge. Sometimes the measurement is as at A: that is, from the *middle* of each wane. Otherwise the method at B is adopted—one wane excluded and the other measured. The matter is one of custom. Shakes and other flaws are all considered in the conversion of the log.

Buying Timber

There are two main ways of buying timber. The first is to select suitable boards at the timber yard and mark out and cut the parts yourself. This is the cheaper, but probably involves your being left with off-cuts. The other way is to give your cutting list to a merchant who supplies against cutting lists. This costs more because the merchant has to select suitable stuff, cut it to size, and is left with short ends. Some merchants plane both sides of the wood but leave sawn edges; others plane the edges as well, though the latter is largely unnecessary because the parts have inevitably to be trimmed to final size, and this means that the machining to exact width is largely wasted. It is clearly the most expensive way of going about it.

It should be realised that a slight alteration in the design can make a great deal of difference to the cost. If you buy planed boards they will obviously be thinner than the sawn timber by the amount removed in chips. There are thus two dimensions: nominal and actual. Boards will measure, say, 25 mm. thick when sawn from a log, but will only be about 22 mm. thick when planed. Thus 22 mm. is actual thickness, although the board will still be known as 25 mm. nominal. This applies specially to softwoods.

4

It follows then that if you design parts of a piece of furniture to finish 25 mm., the merchant will probably have to plane down 32 mm. boards to give the 25 mm. finished thicknesses, and you will have to pay for the waste. In all probability a thickness of 22 mm. would have done just as well.

Allowance for trimming must be made. Edges have to be planed straight and generally made parallel, and this obviously involves waste. The same thing applies to length, though here the allowance may have to be greater (or even less) according to the way in which the item is to be used. Take for instance a framed door. The stiles in which mortises have to be chopped need extra generous allowance in length because the stiles have to project beyond the rails, the waste being sawn off afterwards, and also because chopping mortises close to the end would be liable to cause splitting. On the other hand there is no point in extra allowance in tenoned rails because it would only have to be sawn off before cutting the tenons.

Allowance in width is needed, and here it should be realised that the length affects the amount of allowance. For instance, a rail, say 0·5 m. long, would need only a minimum, whereas a rail 2 m. or so long would need more because even a slight curve in length would need at least 4 mm. extra to allow for planing straight.

As a general guide an allowance of about 15 mm. in lengths is about right (but see special note on rails, stiles, etc.). It could be much less—say 4 mm.—for quite small parts. For widths 5 mm. is ample, though here again the actual size of the parts should be considered. Thicknesses should be the finished size. In the case of squares, such as are needed for legs, etc., always endeavour to work to standard sizes, which are generally: 25 mm., 38 mm., 50 mm., 63 mm., 75 mm., in section. Lengths of such squares are usually 0·50 m., 0·80 m., 1·0 m., 1·2 m. to suit chair, table, and other sizes. Here are some useful rules in brief:

Give dimensions in this order—length, width, thickness. This is practice in cabinet and building trades; timber trade puts thickness first.

Add working allowance to lengths and widths, but give net thicknesses and say so.

Design work to suit standard nominal sizes.

In the final list group together all parts of the same thickness and in the same wood.

When parts have to be jointed give the over-all width (with trimming allowance) and state on list that one or two joints can be allowed, but that grain must be reasonable match.

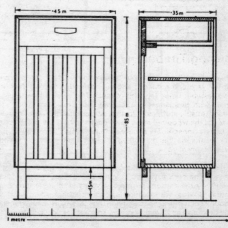

Fig. 1.—Scale elevation of pedestal cupboard in oak. Detail consists of white or black inlay lines. Separated parts are shown on page 6 and cutting lists on page 7.

Cutting lists

Fig. 1 is an item for which a cutting list is needed. In Fig. 2 are shown the actual parts needed, both cutting sizes and final sizes being given. Prepare the cutting list in two stages. In the first the individual parts of carcase, door, drawer, etc., can be grouped together as there is less likelihood of any parts being overlooked. From this the final list is made in which all parts of the same thickness and wood are put together. This enables the merchant (or you, if you are marking the wood yourself) to see exactly how much 22 mm. oak, 16 mm. pine, 4 mm. plywood, or what you will is wanted. It is usual to omit small parts as these can invariably be cut from odd, waste stuff.

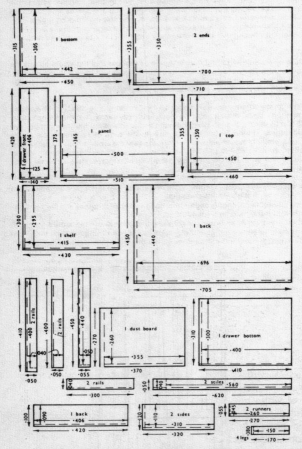

Fig. 2.—Parts of cupboard shown separately. Both cutting sizes with allowances for trimming and final sizes are given.

First cutting list

	long m	wide m	thick mm
2 ends	0·710	0·355	22 oak
1 top	0·460	0·355	22 oak
1 bottom	0·450	0·315	22 pine
1 back	0·705	0·450	12½ ply
1 rail	0·450	0·055	22 oak
2 runners	0·270	0·055	22 pine
1 shelf	0·430	0·300	12½ ply
1 dustboard	0·370	0·270	3 ply
2 stiles	0·620	0·050	22 oak
2 rails	0·400	0·050	22 oak
1 panel	0·375	0·510	12½ ply
1 drawer front	0·420	0·140	22 oak
2 drawer sides	0·320	0·120	10 oak
1 drawer back	0·420	0·100	10 oak
1 drawer bottom	0·410	0·310	4 ply
4 legs	0·170	—	38 sq. oak
2 rails	0·410	0·050	22 oak
2 rails	0·300	0·050	22 oak

Final cutting list

22 mm. figured oak	long m	wide m	
2 pieces	0·710	0·355	⎫ Not more than
1 piece	0·460	0·355	⎬ 2 pieces to make
1 piece	0·450	0·055	up width. Grain
2 pieces	0·620	0·050	reasonable match
1 piece	0·420	0·140	
2 pieces	0·410	0·050	
2 pieces	0·300	0·050	
10 mm. oak			
2 pieces	0·320	0·120	
1 piece	0·420	0·100	
38 mm. sq. oak			
4 pieces	0·170	—	
22 mm. pine			
1 piece	0·450	0·315	
2 pieces	0·270	0·055	
12½ mm. ply			
1 piece	0·705	0·450	
1 piece	0·375	0·510	
1 piece	0·430	0·300	
3 mm. ply			
1 piece	0·370	0·270	
4 mm. ply			
1 piece	0·410	0·310	

Timber Terms

The following terms applied to imperial measurements are given in their nearest metric equivalents. As they are loosely applied to timber, and vary in different trades they cannot be regarded as binding. The sizes are nominal.

Baulk. Timber squared for further conversion and exceeding 115 mm. by 100 mm. Size is usually much larger.

Baulk.

Timber terms

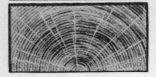

Half-timber. A baulk cut in two along centre.

Flitch. Any large baulk or other timber squared for veneer-cutting or further conversion.

Half-timber.

Wane-edged timber. Partially squared logs with corners not wholly cut out. The outer boards cut from such a timber would have waney edges.

Wane-edged timber.

Slab. The outside slice cut from a log which is being squared or cut into boards. One side rounded.

Slab.

Plank.

Plank. In softwood 280 mm. or more wide by 50–100 mm. thick. In hardwood 50 mm. or more thick.

Deal.

Deal. Softwood from 225–280 mm. wide by 50–100 mm. thick.

Board.

Board. In softwood 100 mm. or more wide and under 50 mm. thick. In hardwood any width and up to 50 mm. thick.

Strip.

Strip. Under 100 mm. wide and under 50 mm. thick.

Batten.

Batten. Width is 100–200 mm. and thickness 50–100 mm. Term is applied to softwoods.

Square.

Square. Square-sectioned timber with sides from 25–150 mm.

Timber terms

Slating batten.

Slating batten. (Also Tiling batten.) Up to 75 mm. wide by 16–32 mm. thick. Common size is 38 mm. or 50 mm. by 19 mm.

Scantling. Width 50–115 mm. and thickness 50–100 mm.

Scantling.

Quarterings. When hardwood such as oak is cut for the purpose of producing figure it is quarter-sawn, as at A (Fig. 1). There are several different methods of sawing. The boards obtained are referred to as "quartered" stuff. Logs of softwood from 225 mm.–300 mm. diameter are quartered, as at B, in large quantities for fence posts. When logs are squared, as at C, the waste sides are termed slabs.

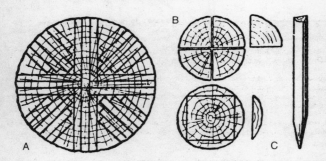

Fig. 1.—A, Quarter-sawn boards. B, Log quartered for fence posts. C, Squared log with waste slabs.

Floor boards vary in width from 100 mm. upwards, 150 mm. being a common size. Thickness, unplaned, except for cheap work, is 25 mm. Boards may be plain-edged (termed P.E.), rebated (R.), or rebated and beaded (R.B.). There is also a special rebated section for secret nailing (see X). The nails holding one board are driven in aslant as indicated, the tongue of the next board covering the head. For superior hardwood flooring the section shown at Z is sometimes used. Boards are also grooved.

Matchboarding also varies in width and thickness from 75 mm. by 16 mm. upwards. Different sections include tongued-and-grooved (T.G.); tongued, grooved, and beaded (T.G.B., the bead being on one or on both sides); tongued, grooved, and V-jointed (T.G.V.J.).

Weatherboarding also varies in width, thickness, and section. The types shown are plain weatherboards (W.B.), rebated (R.W.B.), plain feather-edged (*a*, Fig. 2), shiplap (*b*), log-siding (*c*), planed and moulded (*d*).

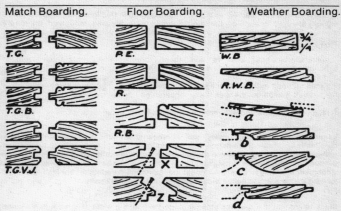

Fig. 2. — Various forms of prepared timber of standard section.

There is also a wide variety of special machined sections for window sashes, door frames, mouldings, and so on.

Plywood consists of three or more layers of veneer glued or cemented together with the grain of each piece laid at right angles to those adjoining. As this reduces (in the stouter thicknesses practically eliminates) any risk of splitting or of shrinkage, the strength of the board is greatly increased.

Plywood is available in thicknesses from 3–6 mm., multi-ply from 8 mm. to 25 mm. In the case of three layers the centre core is usually thicker than the two outer veneers, when

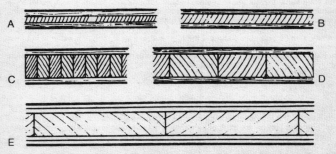

Fig. 3. — Various kinds of laminated wood. *a.* Equal layer plywood *b.* Stout-heart plywood *c.* Laminated board *d.* Block board *e.* Batten board.

Plywood and laminated boards

it is known as stout-heart (B) as distinct from equal-layer (A). When five, seven, or more veneers are used for multi-ply the same thickness of layer is used throughout. Boards are manufactured in standard sized panels, both metric and imperial, and the range varies widely in different countries of origin.

In manufacture birch, alder, ash, and gaboón are widely used. Pine is largely employed in Scandinavia, and Douglas fir is widely used in America.

Faced plywood means that one surface is veneered with a furniture hardwood such as figured oak. Sometimes the back is also veneered with a cheaper veneer.

Marine ply is assembled with resin glue which is highly water-resistant.

Laminated board (C), now largely used for veneered furniture, is built up with the inner core made up of numerous narrow strips glued to each other, both surfaces being faced with a veneer, the grain of which lies at right angles to the core. Alder, birch, poplar, and gaboon are used, and the thicknesses range from 12 mm. to 38 mm. When used for doors, sideboard, and table tops, etc., the edges are lipped and the surfaces veneered. The strips forming the core should not be wider than 7mm. in laminated board.

Block board. In this case the strips forming the core are wider. It is made in the same thicknesses as laminated board, but is less favoured for high-class furniture. From the illustration it will be seen that, both in the case of laminated board and block board, the grain of the core strips is reversed in the gluing. The core strips should not be more than 25 mm. wide in block board, (D).

Batten board. This is a lower grade of built-up board in which the core strips are still wider. It is not so reliable for veneering. The core strips should not be wider than 75 mm., (E).

Wood chipboard. This is made from wood machine chips which are reduced to a fairly small particle size, dried to a constant moisture content, and bonded with synthetic resin under heat and pressure. Wood chipboard is largely used for partitioning and lining, flooring and roofing, fitments, parts of furniture, veneer core, and concrete shuttering; it should not be used out of doors unless protected from the weather. It can be obtained with plain surface, resin paper coated (suitable for a painted finish), plastic surfaced, in shuttering grades, and wood veneered. Normal woodworking tools are used for working it, though precautions are necessary in view of the fairly high density and resin content.

A tungsten carbide tipped tooth is the most suitable for cutting. It is better to cut dead to size as trimming with the plane is awkward owing to the abrasive qualities. The surface should remain untouched except for sanding. If two panels have to be jointed they should be grooved to receive a loose tongue of hardwood or plywood. When panels are joined together at right angles the edge of one piece should stand a trifle proud so that the levelling does not remove shavings from the main surface. The same applies to an edging of solid wood.

Wood chipboard is specially useful for panels which are attached to, or supported by, a framework. It is thus ideal for cabinet backs, wall panels, partitions, etc. If used for structural purposes (say for the ends of a cabinet) it is advisable to apply a substantial lipping of hardwood. Wood chipboard makes a satisfactory base for wood or plastic sheet veneers, but both sides should be covered with veneers of equal thickness. Generally the caul or press should be used rather than the hammer. Sizes and thicknesses of boards vary according to the make, but are mostly to be had in 2·5 m. and in thicknesses 12 mm. and 18 mm., though special thicknesses are available.

Some chipboards are made by the extruded process and usually have veneer facings which should not be cut into as they rely largely upon the facings for their strength.

Veneers

Almost every figured hardwood is normally obtainable in veneers. The finest figured wood, indeed, is rarely on the market in any other form, and many timbers are available only in veneers. The familiar classes of veneer are these:

A. Saw-cut. These are the stoutest, but the most costly: because about 50 per cent. of the log disappears in sawdust. They are not cut to-day because of this reason. Improvements in knife cutting has made the saw obsolete. By cabinet makers they are preferred, this on account of their greater reliability in laying and the avoidance of glue penetration.

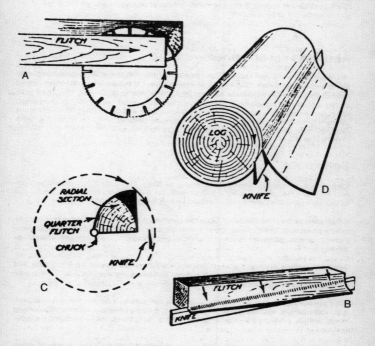

B. Flat knife cut. Like sawn veneers these are cut on the flat, the log being held stationary on a heavy bed while the knife is mounted upon a carriage which slides back and forth. In some cases the knife is stationary whilst the wood moves. The knife cuts across the grain at a slight angle, and the finest figured veneers are produced in this way. Except in cases where the colour might deteriorate (as in sycamore) the timber is steamed before cutting.

C. Half rotary slicing. This method is used for woods which are largely dependent upon being cut on the quarter (that is, in line with the rays) to snow good figure. The log is first quartered, and the quarter segments fixed in the machine with one of the corners nearest the sapwood at the centre. By revolving the segment about this centre the knife cuts a path which is approximately radial. In fact, the middle of each leaf is radial, the edges slightly diverging owing to the curved path of the cut.

Timbers

D. Rotary cut. This is quite a different method, although the veneers are again knife-cut. The logs, about 1·8 metres long, are mounted on a kind of mammoth lathe and a long knife is fed up to it which pares off the veneer. The knife is so held against the revolving log that a sheet of veneer is peeled off its entire length, and the "unrolling" is continued until the core of the log is reached. The grain of the resulting veneer is wild and unnatural, but for plywood these rotary-cut veneers have been found excellent, and they can be produced at a much lower cost than by saw or flat-knife cutting.

A veneer should preferably be laid in the same relative position as when cut from the flitch, though this cannot always be done. For instance, in a quartered panel two of the pieces are bound to be reversed.

Abridged list of timbers

Trees are divided into two distinct families: (1) the coniferous or cone-bearing trees called *softwoods*, which have needle-pointed leaves; (2) the broad-leaved trees termed *hardwoods*, which in temperate climates stand bare during the winter. The terms have chiefly a botanical significance, the porous moisture-conducting deciduous trees being distinguished from the non-porous moisture-absorbing conifers. "Hard" does not imply strength or weight any more than "soft" suggests unreliability or lightness; but the terms have now been accepted universally as convenient for distinguishing the two main families of the timber realm.

Softwoods

Pine (*Pinus sylvestris*). Known alternatively as Scots pine, Scots fir, Red Baltic pine, Red pine, and Redwood. Sources: Scandinavia, the Baltic States, Northern U.S.S.R., and to a lesser extent Scotland. Colour, yellowish white. Weight, 26 lb. per cubic foot.

To us this is the most important timber of commerce. Moderately strong, easily worked, and obtainable in useful dimensions. The carpenter's standard wood for roofing, joists, flooring, beams, partitions, window-frames, doors, fittings, kitchen furniture, and similar work.

Yellow pine (*Pine strobus*). Known also as Canadian pine, Ottawa pine, White pine, and (by agriculturalists) Weymouth pine. Sources: Canada and parts of U.S.A. Colour, pale yellowish white. Weight, 26 lb. Now very scarce.

Pitch pine (*Pinus palustris*). Source: U.S.A. Colour, similar to Scots pine but often with a strongly marked figure. Weight, 42–43 lb. Uses: a constructional wood for shipbuilding work, beams, piles, struts, church pews, spring mattresses, etc. The wood is highly resinous.

Parana pine (*Araucaria angustifolia*). Source: South America. Colour, yellowish, often with reddish streaks. Weight, 30–34 lb. Used for general indoor fitments, but unsuitable for outdoor work. Has good working qualities and can be obtained almost free from knots.

Douglas fir (*Pseudotsuga taxifolia*), commonly known also as British Columbian pine, Oregon pine, Idaho pine, Red pine, Red fir, and Yellow Fir. Source: British Columbia and parts of U.S.A. Colour, somewhat redder than pine. Weight, 32–34 lb.

Douglas fir yields timber for bridge construction, railway carriage wood, ship masts, spars and booms, telegraph and telephone poles, piles, sleepers, decking, flooring, agricultural implements, and carpentry and joinery. The timber is straight-grained and tough and is highly water-resistant.

Spruce (*Picea abies*), commonly designated Whitewood. Sources: Europe, including the

British Isles, Canada, and U.S.A. Colour, cream white. Weight, 28–34 lb. Used extensively for packing-cases, fencing, etc., but also frequently for kitchen table tops, dressers, cupboards, fitments, and flooring.

Sitka spruce (*Picea sitchensis*), known also as Silver spruce. Sources: Western Canada and U.S.A. Weight, 27 lb. Used for house building, agricultural implements, piano sound-boards, organ pipes, oars, paddles, cooperage, butter boxes, kitchen furniture and fitments.

Hemlock (*Tsuga canadensis* and *Tsuga heterophylla*). Sources: Canada, British Columbia, and U.S.A. (N.W.). Colour, pale brown. Weight, 29–30 lb. A general utility softwood, often classed as fir or spruce.

Larch (*Larix decidua*). Sources: Great Britain and Europe generally. Colour, warm light red, often nicely streaked. Weight, 37 lb. The timber is much heavier than pine or spruce. Its principal uses are for outdoor work of all descriptions, including bridges, piles, sleepers, posts, telegraph poles, pit props, farm gates and fencing, agriculture implements, garden fencing, and furnishings, flooring, etc.

Western red cedar (*Thuja plicata*). Source: British Columbia. Colour, pale yellowish brown, turning grey on exposure. Weight, 24 lb.
This timber has many qualities. Left unpainted it does not deteriorate, and it is thus used for complete buildings. Of close, even, and straight grain, it is easy to work and leaves a smooth silky surface. A scented oil renders it free from insect attack, and as it is also resistant to dry rot.

Cedar pencil (*Juniperus virginiana*). Sources: U.S.A. and West Indies. Colour, from pale yellow to pinkish-red. Weight, 33 lb. Used chiefly for pencil making. Under the tool it gives a surface which in smoothness has no equal.

Sequoia (*Sequoia sempervirens*), known generally in America as Redwood. Colour, pinkish-red. Weight, 27 lb. The greatest tree in the world, no special importance attaches to its timber.

Yew (*Taxus baccata*). Source: Europe. Colour, pale red. Weight 42 lb. Uses in early days were for archers' bows, later for doors, panelling, and chairs.

Podo (*Podocarpus gracilior*, etc.). Sources: Uganda. Colour, pale yellow brown. Weight, 32 lb. Used for fitments, joinery, plywood.

Manio (*Podocarpus chiliensis*). Source: Chile. Weight, 35 lb. Colour, light yellow to yellow-brown. Polishes better than most softwoods. Used for joinery, flooring, plywood.

Hardwoods

Abura (*Mitragyna ciliata*). Source: Equatorial Africa. Colour, light brown with pinkish tinge. Weight, 35 lb. Resistant to acids. Used for laboratory work, battery boxes, etc.

Afara (*Terminalia superba*). Source: West Africa. Colour as light oak. Weight, 35 lb. General work. Stains and turns well.

Agba (*Gossweilerodendron balsamiferum*). Source: Nigeria. Colour, yellowish-pink to brown. Weight, 30 lb. Used for furniture, etc.

Alder (*Alnus glutinosa*). Sources: Europe, Asia, and North Africa. Weight, 30–40 lb. A sapwood tree common along the banks of streams. Used for piles; also for clog soles.

Amboyna (*Pterocarpus indicus*). The richly figured burr of the Padauk.

15

Timbers

Apple (*Malus sylvestris*). Sources: Europe and America. Weight, 45 lb. Hard and dense, the timber is used for mallet heads, golf clubs, tool handles, and general turnery. Stained it provides a good substitute for ebony.

Ash (*Fraxinus excelsior*). Source: Europe. Colour, yellowish-white. Weight, 43 lb. Uses: agricultural implements, tool handles, sports goods, etc. Its merits are its long grain and elastic qualities which have made it indispensable for shafts and felloes, agriculture vehicles of all kinds, ladders and poles, axe hafts and tool handles, hockey sticks, croquet mallets, wickets, cask hoops, etc.

Avodire (*Turraeanthus africanus*). Sources: West Africa. Colour, light yellow. Weight, 35 lb. Used for cabinet work, veneer, plywood, etc.

Balsa (*Ochroma lagopus*). Sources: Central and South America. Colour, almost white. Weight, 6–11 lb. Uses: rafts, life-belts, and parts of aircraft. The lightest timber known.

Basswood (*Tilia Americana*). Sources: U.S.A. and Canada. Colour, yellowish white. Weight, 26 lb. It has a considerable use in the pianoforte trade.

Beech (*Fagus sylvatica*). Source: Europe generally. Colour, light yellow. Weight, 45 lb. Uses: chair making, planes, textile machinery work, tool handles, turning, domestic goods, toys. Unsuitable for outdoor work.

Canadian beech (*Fagus grandifolia*) is very largely imported for chair making, lending itself favourably to steam bending.

Birch (*Betula verrucosa* and *Betula pubescens*). Sources: Europe and Canada. Colour, soft brown. Weight, 43 lb. Uses: plywood, chairs, agricultural implements, and general woodwork.

Black bean (*Castanospermum australe*). Source: Queensland, New South Wales. Colour, olive green with dark stripes. Weight, 46 lb. Uses: panelling, doors, fitments, etc.

Blackwood (*Dalbergia melanoxylon*). Source: East Africa. Colour, almost pure black. Weight, about 80 lb. (one of the heaviest known). Uses: musical instruments, knife and surgical instruments handles, turnery.

Boxwood (*Buxus sempervirens*). Sources: Europe and Asia. Colour, a uniform yellow. Weight, 58 lb. Uses: lathe chucks, chessmen, fancy boxes, rules, scales, fine turnery.

Home-grown timber is only available in very small dimensions. The wood is very close and dense and leaves a glossy surface from the plane. Other varieties are imported from West Indies, South Africa, India, and Ceylon. Box is a sapwood.

Canary or American Whitewood (*Liriodendron tulipifera*). Source: U.S.A. (the timber of the tulip tree). Colour, from yellow to greyish-yellow. Uses: interior woodwork, shop fittings, piano work, mouldings, etc.

Cedar (*Cedrela mexicana*). Sources: Mexico, Honduras, Cuba, and Central America generally. Colour, red. Weight, 27–31 lb. Uses: chiefly cigar-box making. The wood has a characteristic fragrance.

Of many cedars the three that are accepted as *true* cedars are (1) the cedar of Lebanon in Syria, (2) the deodar from the Himalaya, (3) the Atlas from the African Atlas Mountains.

Cherry (*Prunus avium*, European, and *Prunus serotina*, American). Sources: Europe generally (the wild cherry, or gean), U.S.A., and Canada. Colour, reddish. Weight, 33–45 lb.

Chestnut (*Castanea sativa*). Sources: Europe generally. Colour, similar to oak. Weight,

35 lb. Uses: indoor woodwork, panelling, etc. This timber (sweet chestnut) must not be confused with horse chestnut.

Cocobolo (*Dalbergia retusa*). Sources: Central and Southern America. Colour, rich red, finely veined. Weight, 60 lb. Uses: musical instruments, knife-handles, small turnery.

Coigue (*Nothofagus dombeyi*). Source: Chile. Colour, similar to the related rauli but lighter. Weight, 36 lb. Used for furniture, turney, etc.

Courbaril (*Hymenaea courbaril*). Sources: West Indies and tropical America. Colour, orange brown. Weight, 50 lb. Used for furniture, turnery, etc.

Dahoma (*Piptadeniastrum africanum*). Sources: Nigeria, Ghana, Cameroon. Colour, golden brown. Weight, 40 lb. Used for structural work, floors, etc.

Ebony (*Diospyros species*). Sources: Southern India, Ceylon, and Burma. Colour, black, interspersed with shades of brown, purple, and grey. Weight (varying), 48–77 lb. Uses: piano keys, walking-sticks, chessmen, boxes, and general ornamental work and turnery. Little is now available for furniture.

Macassar ebony from Indonesia is a richly streaked wood. Coromandel (or calamander) is finely striped ebony from Ceylon.

Elm, British (*Ulmus procera*). Colour, light brown. Weight, 36 lb. Uses: coffins, underwater structures, boat-building, and general construction, including wheelwright's work.

Elm, Wych (*Ulmus glabra*). Source: Europe. Weight, 43 lb. Sometimes known as the Scots elm. Uses are similar to those of the common elm.

Gaboon (*Aucoumea klaineana*). Sources: Equatorial Africa. Weight, 28 lb. Uses: plywood and laminboard, inside parts of furniture. Light, but moderately hard. The French name is *okoumé*.

Greenheart (*Ocotea radiaei*). Sources: Guiana, Brazil. Colour, brown with an occasional green shade. Weight, 67 lb. Uses: shipbuilding, deck, and similar work; but on account of its remarkable elasticity, chiefly for salmon and trout fishing rods.

A somewhat similar timber is Washiba.

Gum, American red, also well known as Satin walnut (*Liquidambar styraciflua*). Source: U.S.A. Colour, mild brown, at times nicely marked. Weight, 37–38 lb. Uses: furniture, panelling, railway carriage work, toys.

The British term "satin walnut" for this timber is now being dropped. The name "hazel pine", applied to the sapwood, is also obsolete.

Hickory (*Carya*, species). Sources: Canada and Eastern U.S.A. Colour, whitish-yellow to yellowish-brown. Weight, 46–47 lb. Uses: shafts and golf clubs, axe, pick, and other handles, oars, bent work, etc.

Holly (*Ilex aquifolium*). Source: Europe generally. Colour, ivory white. Weight, 50 lb. Uses: strings and bandings, turnery, and light work.

Hornbeam (*Carpinus betulus*). Source: Europe, including British Isles. Colour, greenish white; a sapwood. Weight, 43 lb. Uses: engineers' work, skittles, shoe lasts, also piano action work. A strong, tough timber.

Ironbark (*Eucalyptus*, various). Sources: Queensland and New South Wales. Weight, 63–73 lb. Uses: piles, heavy constructional work, sleepers, wagon frames, etc.

Timbers

Jarrah (*Eucalyptus marginata*). Source: Western Australia. Colour, dark red. Weight, 50 lb. Uses: heavy constructional work, wood paving, sleepers; also locally, cabinet work. Strong and durable, the timber is resistant to fire.

Krabak (*Anisoptera*). Sources: Malaya, Burma, Siam. Colour, yellowish brown. Weight, 40 lb. Used for structural work, flooring, etc.

Laburnum (*Laburnum anagyroides*). Sources: British Isles and Europe generally. Colour, rich olive green. Weight, 46–55 lb. Uses almost exclusively for the familiar "oysters" seen on decorative veneers.

Laurel (*Terminalia alata*). Sources: India and Burma. Colour, from warm yellow to brown, handsomely figured. Weight, varies from 50 to 55 lb. Uses: high-class office and library fittings, panelling, furniture.

Lignum vitae (*Guaiacum officinale*). Sources: West Indies and tropical America. Colour, dark brown, streaked with black. Weight, 73–80 lb. Uses: axle bearings, bushes, bowling balls, ornamental cups, pulley blocks, turnery.

Lime (*Tilia vulgaris*). Sources: Europe, including British Isles. Colour, yellowish-white. Weight, 37–38 lb. Uses: piano case work, artificial limbs, carving, and turnery.

Mahogany, Cuban (*Swietenia mahogani*). Source: Cuba. Weight, 40 lb. Hard and somewhat brittle, with white deposit in the grain. A splendid furniture wood but now scarce

Mahogany, Central American (*Swietenia macrophylla*). Sources: Honduras, Mexico, Panama, Tobasco, Brazil, Peru, etc. Weight, 34–39 lb. An excellent furniture wood but now often available only in veneer. Sometimes beautifully marked.

Mahogany, African (*Khaya ivorensis*). Source: West Africa. Weight, from 30 to 38 lb. Widely used for furniture and fitments but has not the fine figure of the Central American variety and not so reliable.

Makoré (*Mimusops heckelii*). Source: West Africa. Colour, pinkish-brown to purple-brown. Weight, 39 lb. Used for furniture, veneers, interior fittings, etc.

Maple (*Acer*, various). Sources: Canada and U.S.A.; also Europe. Colour, varied yellow. Weight, 37 lb. Uses: textile trade work, billiard cues, violins, letter blocks, shoe lasts, turnery; also suitable for flooring. "Bird's eye" maple with its beautiful mottled figure, is cut from the Rock maple (*Acer saccharum*).

Meranti (*Shorea*). Sources: Malaya and Sarawak. Colour, light straw and dark brown. Weight, 32–41 lb. Used for furniture, etc.

Nyankom (*Tarrietia utilis*). Sources: Gold Coast, Sierra Leone. Colour, pale reddish brown. Weight, 40 lb. Uses: cabinet work, structural work, etc.

Oak, British (*Quercus robur*). British Isles. Weight, 45–52 lb.

Oak, European (*Quercus robur*). Sources: Baltic States, Russia, Poland, Hungary, Yugoslavia, etc. Weight, averaging 47 lb.

Oak, American (*Quercus rubra*) red, and (*Quercus alba*) white. Sources: U.S.A. and Eastern Canada. Weight, 45–50 lb.

Oak, Japanese (*Quercus mongolica*). Southern Japan. Weight, 40–47 lb.

Oak, Silky (*Cardwellia sublimis*). Australia. Weight, 37 lb. Not a true oak.

Although for strength and durability British Oak is unsurpassed the consumption in this country is almost negligible compared with that of imported oaks. Apart from high-class furniture (timber from the straight woodland trees) its principal uses are for ship-building, barge and boat work, roof trusses, railway wagon and carriage construction, wheelwright's work, outdoor parts, and general construction work.

The Northern European oaks, differing only slightly from the British variety, are shipped mainly from Danzig and Riga, the so-called Austrian or Hungarian timbers being derived from the Crotian and Slavonian forests.

Of American oak there are several varieties, all lighter in weight than European oak. Japanese oak is imported for household furniture and similar work.

Obeche (*Triplochiton scleroxylon*). Source: Cameroon. Colour, light straw. Weight, 20–24 lb. Used for cabinet work, veneering grounds, plywood core, etc.

Olive (*Olea hochstetteri*). Source: East Africa. Colour, rich yellowish brown. Uses: chiefly fancy boxes, cigar and cigarette cases, brush backs, etc.

Opepe (*Sarcocephalus diderrichii*). Source: West Africa. Colour, yellow brown. Weight, 46 lb. Used for interior fittings, floorings, etc.

Padauk (*Pterocarpus dalbergioides*). Sources: Andaman Islands and Burma. Colour, usually a brilliant red, with darker streaks, but frequently turns to a greyish black on exposure. Weight, 54–59 lb. Uses: bank and office fittings, panelling; also used locally for building purposes, cart frames, spokes and felloes.

Pear (*Pyrus communis*). Source: Europe generally. Colour, pale reddish yellow. Weight, 47–48 lb. Uses: chiefly carving, T-squares, set-squares, draughtsman's curves, etc. Grain is short and close, cutting sharp in every direction.

Plane, London (*Platanus acerifolia*). Source: Europe, including British Isles. Colour, light yellow to pale red. Weight, 40 lb. Uses: shuttles, shoe lasts, golf club heads, turnery. Cut on the quarter, richly figured and mottled plane is often termed "lace-wood".

Plum (*Prunus domestica*). Source: Europe generally. Colour, brownish-red, nicely streaked. Weight, 50–53 lb. Uses: tool handles, turnery.

Poplar (*Populus*, various). Sources: British Isles, Europe, Canada, and U.S.A. Colour, whitish yellow and whitish grey. Weight, 28 lb. Uses: chiefly packing-cases and toys, formerly for inlaying.

Prima vera (*Cybistax donnell-smithii*). Sources: Honduras and Central America. Colour, yellowish white to brown. Weight, 31 lb. Used for interior fitments, furniture, etc.

Purpleheart (*Peltogyne species*). Sources: West Indies, Central and South America. Colour, pale brown when first cut, but changes rapidly to purple. Weight, 56 lb. Used for furniture, turnery, fancy work.

Queensland walnut (*Endiandra palmerstonii*). Source: North Queensland. Colour, walnut brown. Weight, 42 lb. Used for furniture-making, joinery, etc. Saw teeth and edges are blunted quickly.

Ramin (*Gonystylus*). Source: Sarawak. Colour, light yellow. Weight, 42 lb. Used for furniture mainly.

Rauli (*Nothofagus procera*). Source: Chile. Colour, light red-brown. Weight, 38 lb. Used for furniture, turnery, etc.

Timbers

Rosewood (*Dalbergia*, various). Sources: Brazil, Honduras, and East Indies. Colour, dark purple brown, banded with stripy markings. Weight, 53–63 lb. according to variety. Uses (almost wholly in veneer form): piano cases, cabinets, ornamental boxes, inlaying, etc. In this country the East Indian rosewood is now more widely used.

Sapele (*Entandrophragma cylindricum*). Source: East and West Africa. Colour, birch brown. Weight, 44 lb. Uses: interior furniture parts, veneering. The trees grow to a great height, many producing squared logs of six feet.

Satin walnut. (See Gum.)

Satinwood, East Indian (*Chloroxylon swietenia*). Sources: Ceylon, India, Burma. Colour, rich yellow. Weight, 59 lb.

Satinwood, West Indian (*Fagara flava*). Sources: Bahamas, Jamaica, San Domingo, and Puerto Rico. Weight, 51–52 lb. Uses: Employed chiefly in veneer form and for inlay stringings.

Sycamore (*Acer pseudoplatanus*). Sources: British Isles and Europe generally. Colour, nearly milk white, often richly mottled. Weight, 38–39 lb. Uses: flooring, textile trade work, rollers, cabinet work, ship-cabin fitments, dairy utensils, domestic goods, turnery.
   The dyed grey wood fasionable for furniture (occasionally called "harewood") is produced from sycamore.

Teak (*Tectona grandis*). Sources: Burma, India, etc. Colour, brown, sometimes straw, but tending to darken on exposure. Weight, 45 lb. Uses: shipbuilding, railway work, building construction, high-class joinery, gates, garden furniture, etc.

   One of the most valuable timbers of the world, teak has an enormous consumption, and being strongly fire-resistant and immune from the attack of the white ant, its uses cover almost every department of woodwork. Its resistance to crushing and transverse strain has earned for it the reputation of being the strongest timber available.

Walnut, European (*Juglans regia*). Sources: Great Britain, France, Italy, Black Sea area, etc. Weight, 40–46 lb. Purple-brown colour. Used for furniture but difficult to obtain in the solid. Often richly figured.

Walnut, American black (*Juglans nigra*). Source: Eastern U.S.A. Weight, 37–38 lb. A fine furniture wood.

Walnut, African (*Lovoa Klaineana*). Alternatively known as Nigerian walnut, tigerwood, congowood, etc. Source: West Africa. Weight, 31 lb.

Walnut, Japanese (*Juglans sieboldiana*). Source: chiefly Manchuria. Weight, 32 lb.

Willow (*Salix alba*, etc.). Sources: Europe, including British Isles; also (a different variety) U.S.A. Colour, pale greyish-yellow. Weight, 24–25 lb. Uses (according to species): cricket bats, basket work. The wood is strongly resistant to splitting.

Manufactured boards

   There is a wide range of proprietary boards made for various purposes, some of them being used nowadays as substitutes for solid wood for certain uses. The materials with which they are made varies with the uses for which they are intended, and should be considered when a selection is made. Some are intended for outdoor use, being able to resist most weather conditions, others are for indoor work only. The majority are not structural boards, but are meant mostly as filling panels for framework of solid wood or metal, and they should not be called upon to do work for which they are unsuited.

Manufactured boards

Asbestos-cement board. Suitable for outdoor use, it is made in flat sheets suitable for walls and partitions, and in corrugated form for roof work. It is somewhat brittle, however, and should therefore not be used in positions where it may be subjected to rough treatment. Rigid fixing is not advisable because any movement in the framing to which it is fixed may cause cracking. The better plan is to allow a 5 mm. gap between adjacent panels and cover with a wood fillet, the fixing nails passing through the gap. If nails through the sheet are essential holes rather larger than the nails should be drilled. Take care not to shatter the panel with the hammer, especially when the nail is nearly home. Corrugated sheets are fixed with 90 mm. galvanised screws driven through holes drilled through crown of the corrugations (not the valleys) with special washers to keep out water. If possible the board should be used in the standard sizes as it is awkward stuff to cut. A small-toothed saw *can* be used but it is hard on tools. Sizes vary in different makes.

Asbestos fibre board. This has a high fibre content making it more easily workable than asbestos-cement board. Nails can be driven through it without previous drilling, and it can be sawn or cut by scribing with a knife along the line after which it will break. It can also be bent within certain limits. It is suitable for outhouses, poultry houses, garages, sheds, partitions, and so on. For roofs the corrugated type should be used. Sizes and thicknesses vary.

Fibre building board. Under this heading is a wide range of proprietary materials ranging from comparatively soft boards used largely for their insulation value to really hard boards suitable for van bodies, trailer caravans, etc. Various materials—wood, straw, cane, and other vegetable products—are used in its manufacture. They are not structural and require to be fixed to a rigid framework. Ordinary woodworking tools are used for cutting, though holes are best made with the morse drill used for metal work. Sizes and thicknesses vary widely.

The chief headings under which they are classified are:

Insulating board. Density not exceeding 25 lb. per cubic foot and nominal thickness of not less than 12 mm.

Wall board. Density not exceeding 30 lb. per cubic foot and usually 4 mm. to 10 mm. thick.

Hardboard. Density between 30 and 50 lb. Thicknesses in common use are about 3 mm. and 5 mm., but thicker boards are also available. A specially compressed and impregnated variety is also available, this being suitable for outdoor work such as caravans, etc.

Embossed board is also made, this having a pattern such as reeding formed in the surface whilst under compression. Perforated board having small holes drilled at regular intervals is used widely for shop display work and so on.

Plastic laminate. Used for table and cabinet tops, wall panels, and so on. Mostly made from paper sheets heavily compressed and impregnated with resin. Many of them are highly resistant to heat so that a lighted cigarette could be laid on them without damage. This gives them a special value for table tops, etc. Some varieties are obtainable in colours and in special finishes such as linen, onyx, wood grain. Panel sizes and thickness (about 1·5 mm. and upwards) vary according to make.

Most hardboards, chipboards, and so on can be assembled with animal or resin glue, the usual technique being followed. Plastic boards to be fixed to wood call for the use of contact adhesive or synthetic resin.

Glass. The type of glass used for glazing windows is known as sheet glass, and is normally obtainable in three grades: best (used for good quality work); seconds (for general average work); and thirds (often used in greenhouses, garden frames, etc.). Its thickness is known by the weight of glass in a square foot. Thus a piece of glass 24 in. by 12 in.

Useful chemicals

weighing 30 oz. is known as 15-oz. glass. The latter is used in the smallest work only, being liable to fracture if used in larger sizes. For the general run of windows 21 oz. is the thinnest practicable size, and this should be increased to 26 oz. in good work. For larger panes 32 oz. is desirable. As a general guide, 15-oz. glass is full 1·58 mm. thick; 18 oz.–2·1 mm.; 21 oz.–2·5 mm. bare; 24 oz.–2·5 mm. full; 26 oz.–3·2 mm.; 32 oz.–4·0 mm.; 42 oz.–5·0 mm.

There are many other varieties of glass made for special purposes, such as reeded, cathedral, and figure rolled, which obscure the vision to a degree according to the type. Also wired glass made in varying meshes; toughened glass; tinted glass; glass slates and tiles; prismatic, and so on.

Sheet glass is inclined to distort objects seen through it, especially seconds and thirds, and for the best work plate glass is advisable. This is made of better materials, and is ground flat and polished. It is made in thicknesses from 5 mm. upwards.

Useful chemicals

P = poisonous; *C* = harmful to touch.

Acetic acid. 6% used in some furniture revivers. Vinegar is an impure form of acetic acid.

Alkanet root. Used chiefly for making red oil. The roots are 4–6 in. long and anything up to ½ in. thick. They are bruised and steeped in linseed oil. Difficult to obtain.

American potash is used for the weathering of oak. It turns the wood deep brown, causing the figure to become almost black. Subsequent treatment with chloride of lime turns it grey. It is now often known under the name of crude caustic potash. *P.C.*

Ammonia. Used chiefly for fuming oak, but is also useful for adding to water stain, as it helps to drive the latter into the grain. Obtain 0·880 (ask for "point eight-eighty" ammonia) and keep well corked, as it speedily loses its strength when exposed to the air. Rock ammonia is used for polish strippers. *P.C.*

Aniline dyes are obtainable in many colours and soluble in water, spirits, or oil. The kind required should be stated when ordering.
Black, blue, crimson, magenta, orange, red, yellow, bismarck brown, vandyke brown, green, maroon, purple.
The dyes are used for making stains and for tinting polish. Colours can be blended, but water-, oil-, and spirit-soluble dyes cannot be mixed. *P* usually.

Asphalt see *Liquid asphalt and pitch*.

Benzoin or gum benzoin. A resin used for making polisher's glaze. It is in the form of small pieces and looks like dried twigs compressed together in which are white specks. The more of the latter the better the quality.

Benzine. Sometimes used to remove excessive oil in varnishing. *P.*

Berlin black. A thick black liquid which dries out flat without shine.

Bichromate of potash. Purchased in crystal form, of a deep orange shade. Used chiefly for darkening mahogany. Can also be used for oak. *P.*

Bismarck brown. An aniline dye of fiery red colour. If used too strong it has a greenish hue. It is powerful, and should be used cautiously. *P.*

Bitumen powder, also called mineral pitch. Used for repeat designs for marquetry.

22

Borax. Used in some strippers; also for water varnishes. Sometimes used to neutralise oxalic acid after bleaching.

Brown umber. A brown pigment which can be worked up in water or turpentine. Mixed with water and bound with glue size it makes a cheap water coating for inexpensive furniture backs.

Brunswick black. A thick black liquid drying with a shine. Used in woodwork for floor stains, for which purpose it is thinned out.

Burnt sienna. Pigment powder, light red-brown colour. Used much as brown umber.

Burnt umber. Similar to brown umber, but of deeper, stronger tone.

Butter of antimony. A dark brown liquid which has a slight hardening effect on polish. Used in making furniture revivers. *P.C.*

Camphor. Used in some furniture revivers. *P.*

Camphorated oil. A mixture of four parts olive oil and one part camphor. Used for the removal of heat and water marks. *P.*

Carbon tetrachloride. For degreasing some woods before gluing. It is used chiefly on teak, the greasy nature of which prevents glue from sticking well. *P.C.*

Carborundum powder. An abrasive obtainable in various grades. The fine grade is used in making the black coating for blackboards to give a bite to the chalk. Also used for rubbing down worn oilstones.

Caustic potash. Used as a stripper for polish, paint, etc. It tends to darken some woods and should be used with care. *P.C.*

China clay. Used for making paste wood filler.

Chloride of lime. Imparts a greyish tone to oak. Is used in the weathered finish.

Copal. A gum used in the manufacture of varnishes which have an oil basis. It comes from Africa and is a pale, yellowish resin, though some varieties are darker.

Copperas (green) (sulphate of iron). A chemical crystal which, dissolved in water, gives a pale blue shade. Used for killing the redness in mahogany when the latter has to imitate walnut. Also for staining oak a blue-grey colour. Turns sycamore a grey tone, thus producing greywood or harewood. *P.*

Creosote. An oily liquid obtained from wood tar. Used as a preservative for wood.

Crocus powder. A fine abrasive used for dusting over a polished surface to dull it. Also used as a strop dressing for carving tools.

Dragon's blood. A red agent for colouring polishes. It has been largely superseded by aniline dyes.

Drop black. Obtained in the form of a thick paste which is thinned with turps. It is used sometimes in ebonising and in the preparation of blackboards.

Emery powder. An abrasive sometimes used in the preparation of blackboards. It gives a bite to the chalk. Also used for rubbing down varnished work. The fine grade mixed with lubricating oil makes an effective dressing for tool strops. Also sometimes used on oilstones which have lost their cut.

Useful chemicals

Eosin powder. A red powder dissolved in water and used to warm water stains. *P.*

Flake white. A white powder sometimes mixed with white polish for lightening the tone of the wood. Mixed with Scotch glue it turns the latter white, making it suitable for light woods. *P.*

French chalk. A finely powdered white chalk used in making the half-filling for oak to be french polished. Also sometimes used to lubricate surfaces which rub together.

Fuller's earth. Used in varnishing for removing oiliness.

Gas black. A preparation made by suspending a sheet of tin over a fishtail gas burner. Used chiefly in ebonising.

Glue size. Sometimes used as a partial filling on deal before the application of polish. Also used in the preparation of water coatings, in which it acts as a binder. It is also applied to softwoods to be veneered and to end grain.

Gold size. A quick-drying varnish normally used for the application of gold leaf and gold paint. It is also a useful binder for colours ground in turps. Sometimes used in making paste fillers.

Gum benzoin. See benzoin.

Hydrogen peroxide. Used for bleaching. 100 vol. is generally used, diluted with 2 parts water. Some chemists supply not less than 2 gallons. *P.C.*

Hyposulphite of soda. Sometimes useful for removing stains made by iodine.

Lamp black. A black powder used for water coating, also in ebonising.

Lime. Unslaked lime is used for the limed oak finish. Also used in the antique oak finish. *P.C.*

Linseed oil is derived from the seed of the flax plant and can be obtained either raw or boiled. It takes up oxygen on exposure to the air and is thus a *drying* oil. Boiling the oil makes it dry more rapidly. It is used in the french polish process for killing the whiteness of filler, in lubricating the rubber, and for making red oil. It is also used in oil polishing and in the manufacture of putty. Paint makers use the raw oil for light shades, and boiled oil for darker tones. It makes an excellent lubricant for tools and can be applied with a wad of cottonwool.

Raw linseed oil is somewhat viscid, fairly clear, and is brownish-yellow in colour. It is used for lubricating the rubber in polishing.

Boiled linseed oil is of a reddish-brown tinge and is rather more viscid than the raw. It is used in oil polishing.

Liquid asphalt. For making brown stains. Thinned with turps

Litharge. A pinkish powder used in colouring. *P.*

Logwood. The heartwood of a tree found in Central America which, when cut into chips, is soaked and boiled in water. It is used as a basis for stains, but discretion must be used, since its shade varies in accordance with other substances with which it comes into contact. It may vary from red, straw colour, purple, to black.

Mahogany crystals. Obtainable in crystal form and dissolved in warm water to make a reddish-brown stain. *P.*

Mastic. A resinous gum, pale yellow in colour when fresh and inclining to darken when kept. It is used in varnish making.

Methylated spirits. This is used mostly for making french polish and stains. It is ordinary alcohol with wood spirit, etc., added to make it undrinkable, in which form it is sold free of duty. There are several kinds of mixtures produced for various purposes permitted by the Customs and Excise, and they are all subject to regulations. French polish manufacturers use industrial methylated spirits, known as "I.M.S.", but this is not obtainable by the general public. That sold in oil shops is coloured and is made further unpalatable by the addition of wood spirit, mineral spirit, pyridine, and methyl violet dye. French polish can be made with this successfully because the colouring effect is small and soon fades. A better method, however, is to use "methylated finish." This is colourless, but contains three ounces of resin per gallon. This resin may be common rosin (this is the more usual, as it is a cheaper substance) or it may be white lac. For the purpose of polish making "methylated spirit white lac" is more suitable, and can generally be obtained if specified. *P.*

Mineral oil. See white mineral oil.

Naphtha. Used sometimes in spirit varnishing to remove ridges. *P.*

Nigrosine crystals. Used for making a dark stain, particularly for oak. The crystals are dissolved in warm water. Colour is cold brown. *P.*

Nitric acid. A chemical sometimes used in the manufacture of stain and for removing ink marks. *P.*.

Ox gall. Used in the acid finish for french polish.

Oxalic acid. Used chiefly for bleaching wood and for removing stains. It is bought in the form of small crystals, these being dissolved in warm water. Being a poison, care should be taken not to leave it about, and to avoid contact with the fingers. If this cannot be avoided wash well after using. *P.*

Paraffin, medicinal. Used as a lubricant for the polishing rubber on light woods.

Pearl ash. Sometimes used for stripping off old polish, varnish, etc.

Permanganate of potash. Obtained in the form of fine crystals. It is sometimes used for making a stain, producing a deep, rich brown, but it is not really satisfactory as the colour is fugitive. *P.*

Pitch. Asphalt in lump form, makes a brown stain.

Plaster of paris. Used chiefly as a filler before polishing. The "super-fine" grade obtainable at most oil shops should be used. It must be kept in a dry place.

Poppy oil. Preferred by some workers as a lubricant for the polishing rubber.

Potash. See under American, caustic, bichromate, etc.

Powder colours. These are used chiefly for tinting plaster of paris, when making wood filler, though they are also handy for water coatings. Useful colours are vandyke brown, brown umber, burnt umber, raw sienna, yellow ochre, venetian red, red ochre, lamp black, flake white.

Precipitated chalk. See note under Vienna chalk.

Pumice powder. A white powder obtainable in various grades. It is useful as a fine abrasive and is sometimes used in the polishing and varnishing processes for taking out the

Useful chemicals

roughness of a surface. The usual plan in polishing is to use it in a pounce bag, this being dabbed on to the work leaving a fine deposit of powder which is taken up by the polishing rubber. The finest grade should be used.

Pyrogallic acid. Sometimes used in the fuming process, producing a warm tone.

Reckitt's blue. Used in the ebonising process to make the black polish a deeper and more intense black.

Red oil. See alkanet root.

Red sanders. The heartwood of an Indian tree. Small splinterings are used for dyeing the spirits used in making french polish, producing a blood-red shade.

Rose pink. A powder colour used for tinting plaster of paris filling.

Rosin. The hard resin left after distilling off the oil of turpentine. Sometimes added to wax polish to give a harder finish. Also used in making stopping.

Rottenstone. A fine abrasive (finer than pumice powder) and sometimes used in the pounce bag (see Tripoli powder).

Russian tallow. Occasionally used as a filler, but it never hardens properly. Often used in polishing coffins.

Sandarac. A pale yellow resin used in making spirit varnish.

Shellac. This is the basis of all french polishes. Most of it comes from the Calcutta and Mirzapore districts, and is derived from the exudation of the lac insect. It varies in colour considerably. White shellac is merely an orange shellac bleached with chemicals to lighten it and "pulled out" in a similar method to that used by the toffee maker, and looks rather like sticks or knots of thick white toffee. It should be kept under water or stored in damp sawdust, as it quickly becomes denatured if exposed to the air. The other shellacs are in the form of thin flakes. The following are the shellacs normally obtainable, given in the order of their colour: white, orange, button, garnet. The button shellac has the reputation for being rather harder than the others, but is inclined to make a somewhat cloudy polish.

Silex. A powder substance used in making paste filler.

Soda. Ordinary washing soda is useful for removing grease from a surface. It must not be used strong or it will strip off polish, and all traces must be washed off with clear water.

Sodium perborate. Can be used in the bleaching process.

Spirit black, chrysoidine, green, mahogany, walnut. Can be obtained in powder or liquid form. The former is dissolved in methylated spirit. Used for staining. A little french polish is added to fix the stain.

Spirits of camphor. Used in furniture revivers. Large dose may be *P.*

Sulphate of iron. See copperas.

Sulphuric acid. Used for the acid finish in french polishing. Add the acid drop by drop to water. *P.C.*

Tannic acid. Used sometimes in fuming oak.

Terebine. A drying agent sometimes used in correcting faults in varnished work. *P.*

Toppings. The clear liquid suspended above the stock solution of white french polish. It is strained off the polish and used as a finishing glaze.

Tripoli powder. A fine abrasive used to dull the extreme gloss of french polished work.

Turpentine. Used for making many oil stains and in making wax polish. Many substitutes are on the market owing to the high cost of pure turps, and many contain oils of the petroleum class which may act as a bleaching agent. Pure American turpentine is the best. See also white spirit.

Vandyke brown. A brown powder used for making stains and for water coatings. It will not mix directly with water. Add it to ammonia to form a paste and mix this with warm water and glue size. A better stain is made with vandyke crystals (q.v).

Vandyke crystals. Obtainable in fairly coarse crystals and makes a deep brown stain.

Venetian red. Used for mixing with plaster of paris filler to tint to a reddish tone.

Vienna chalk. Used in conjunction with sulphuric acid in the acid finish for french polish. As a substitute use precipitated chalk.

Vinegar. Frequently used in furniture revivers. It helps to remove grease, oil, etc. See also acetic acid.

Walnut crystals. See vandyke crystals.

Wax. Used in wax polishing. The chief kinds are: beeswax, bleached and unbleached; Japan wax; ozokerite wax; paraffin wax; and carnauba wax.
Beeswax. The unbleached wax is of a yellow to brown colour suitable for dark woods. For light woods bleached wax should be used. Beeswax is the basis of most wax polishes.
Japan Wax. Sometimes mixed with beeswax in making wax polishes.
Ozokerite Wax. A natural earth wax also used with beeswax.
Paraffin Wax. A petroleum product of a whitish colour, used for light wax polishes.
Carnauba Wax. A vegetable product used for making wax polish harder. In purified form it is of a pale yellowish shade. Polish made entirely with carnauba wax gives a very hard finish, but with repeated coats is inclined to flake. It is more satisfactory used with softer waxes. Wax is also used in making stopping.

White mineral oil. Used as a lubricant for the rubber when french polishing.

White spirit (turps substitute). Used in making some oil stains and for cleaning old woodwork. It should be as free of grease as possible. Test by soaking blotting paper and leave to dry. Good quality will dry out without residue. Greasy turps will leave a greasy deposit.

Whiting. Used in making putty and for some wood fillers. A superfine quality is also used in the manufacture of gesso.

Yellow ochre. A powder colour used in colouring wood fillers and for water coating.

Zinc white. A powder added to Scotch glue to whiten it for use on light-coloured woods. Can also be used with wax to form the deposit in the limed oak finish.

Polishes, lacquers, etc.

Modern proprietary finishes have largely replaced traditional polishes, though the last-named are still used in some trades, especially in repair and antique workshops. In all proprietary finishes it is essential to follow the maker's instructions regarding stains, fillers, avoidance of oil, etc.

Wood finishing recipes

Polyurethane lacquer. A tough finish which resists water, spirit, and heat marking. According to type it may be a two-can lacquer, the base and the hardener; or a one-can kind which is used straight from the can. There are varieties for spraying, brushing, or fadding. It is essential to use the recommended stains and fillers.

Polyster lacquer. A hard durable yet flexible finish, resistant to wear, liquid marking and heat. Up to the present its use has been confined to the factory owing to complications in its application.

Plastic coating. A finish based on synthetic resin which dries by chemical reaction. It is resistant to hard usage, heat and liquid marking. It is brush-applied.

Cellulose lacquer. A tough finish which, according to type, may be spray-, brush-, or rubber applied.

French polish. A finish formerly widely used for furniture and still used by restorers and repairers, it is capable of an excellent finish but is neither heat- nor spirit-resistant. The main types are:

orange, a golden brown shade; *button*, yellowish and slightly opaque; *garnet*, deep brown colour; *white*, slightly milky-white for light woods; *transparent*, water-clear; *black*, tinted black for ebonising; *red*, orange polish tinted with spirit-soluble aniline dye; *glaze*, 6 oz. crushed gum benzoin in 1 pint methylated spirit.

Wax polishes

There are many excellent proprietary wax polishes but for those who prefer to make their own the following are given. Note that in all cases time should be allowed after application for the turps to evaporate as no shine can be built up until this has occurred.

When waxing over oil stain, fix the latter first with one or two rubbers of french polish or use a sealer. Otherwise the stain may be lifted in patches.

Light polish. Shred bleached beeswax. Dissolve in turpentine (best American) to form thin paste (like butter in summer-time).

Normal polish. Substitute unbleached beeswax in the above.

Brown polish. Shred unbleached beeswax. Dissolve in turpentine, making thin paste. Add raw or burnt umber powder, and stir thoroughly.

Antique (black) polish. Shred unbleached beeswax. Dissolve in turpentine, forming thin paste. Add lamp black powder and stir thoroughly.

The dissolving of the wax in any of the above recipes can be speeded by warming the mixture in a jar of hot water. Keep it away from a naked flame.

Any of the polishes above can be hardened by the addition of carnauba wax. The proportion could be one carnauba wax to three or four beeswax.

Another way of hardening polish is to add a small amount of powdered rosin dissolved with the wax.

Petrol (as used in lighters) is sometimes added to wax polish to speed up evaporation.

Stains, etc.

Although ready-made stains are widely used nowadays owing to their reliability and to the wide range available, the following still hold their own, partly because they are inexpensive and partly because they have never been improved upon for certain purposes. They are widely used in the trade.

Vandyke crystals. Give a rich brown colour, varying from a deep tone to a light shade. Ideal for oak, walnut (used weak), and occasionally for cold tones of mahogany. Also for deal or plywood to match oak or walnut.

Dissolve vandyke crystals in warm water (amount depends upon depth required). Strain through muslin. Add dash of 0·880 ammonia (ask for "point eight-eighty ammonia"). The ammonia helps to drive the stain into the grain. Keep the stain well corked after the ammonia has been added. Vandyke crystals are also known as walnut crystals.

Bichromate of potash. Widely used to darken mahogany, to which it gives a somewhat cold brown tone, depth of which may be varied according to strength. Can also be used for oak, to which it gives a slightly greenish-brown tone.

Dissolve bichromate of potash crystals in water to make a concentrated solution (that is, water will absorb no more), bottle, and dilute as required.

Use in daylight. Some varieties of the same wood are more affected than others. Mixed woods should therefore be avoided. It is sometimes useful after fuming to correct unevenness in tone. Both crystals and stain are deep orange colour which bears no relation to the shade produced in the wood. Most softwoods and some hardwoods are not affected by it.

Green copperas (sulphate of iron). Gives oak a blue-grey tone. Crystals are dissolved in water which becomes a muddy green colour. Effect on wood shows only as it dries out. Try on spare piece of same wood first. Fix with two coats of white french polish before filling in with plaster of paris and water.

Aniline dyes. Obtainable in powder form in many colours and soluble in water, methylated spirits, or oil. Avoid colours which are unorthodox for woodwork. Vandyke brown is the most useful. To warm this add a *little* bismarck brown (this is a fiery red). For a colder tone add black. Make up each stain separately and mix the liquids as required. Other colours sometimes useful are yellow, green, blue, mauve, red; but use with caution or the result may be startling

Spirit stain. Dissolve aniline spirit powder in methylated spirit (amount according to tone). Strain through muslin. Add dessertspoonful of french polish to each pint of stain to bind it. The stain dries rapidly so that a quick, deft touch is needed.
Water stain. Dissolve aniline water powder in warm water (amount according to tone). Strain through muslin. Add dessertspoonful of hot glue and a dash of vinegar. Use warm.
Oil stain. Dissolve aniline oil powder in turpentine. Heat in hot water (not naked flame). Strain through muslin. Add dessertspoonful gold size.

Order the aniline due in accordance with the liquid with which it is to be mixed – spirit, water, or oil.

Ammonia. Generally used in fuming, but will slightly darken oak and mahogany if applied as a liquid. Use 0·880 ("point eight-eighty"). Avoid touching with the fingers as it may turn them yellow and be painful.

Asphaltum. Gives a brown stain suitable for softwood to resemble oak. Crush lamp asphaltum and dissolve in turpentine. Strain through muslin, and add dessertspoonful gold size to pint of stain. Dissolving will be quickened if turpentine is heated in hot water away from naked flame.

Fuming. Used mostly for oak which it turns a deep and rather cold brown. Shade may be anything from a light tone to almost black. Some varieties of oak take to it more than

Wood finishing recipes

others. English, Austrian, Japanese, and American white oak are all affected by it. American red oak is the least affected of the oaks.

Prepare an airtight box or chamber, and insert work and two to three saucers of 0·880 ("point eight-eighty ammonia"). Close up and leave till colour is reached.

To save opening door insert dowel of same kind of oak through hole. Withdraw occasionally to see progress. Avoid standing over cupboard when opening as fumes are strong. Remove all grease and glue from wood before fuming, and avoid overlapping parts. Do not dip fingers in ammonia as it can be painful.

Process can be quickened as follows:
Dissolve 1 oz. tannin powder in 1 quart water, and apply to surface like stain. Fume in chamber.

or

Dissolve ½ oz. pyrogallic acid in 1 quart water, and apply to surface like stain. Fume in chamber.
The pyrogallic acid treatment gives a redder tone than the tannic acid. A mixture of the two gives a slightly different shade from either.

Floor stain. For a new floor the following is effective:
Dissolve vandyke crystals in 1 pint warm water. Add a good tablespoonful of 0·880 ammonia. Add tablespoonful of hot Scotch glue. Use warm.

or

Burnt umber ground in oil. Thin with linseed oil and turps. Add a little liquid drier. When dry rub off surface grease with coarse cloth and give coat of spirit varnish.
For a mahogany colour substitute venetian red for burnt umber.

Red oil. For giving warmth and lustre to pale baywoods which are to resemble mahogany.
Add a little bismarck brown aniline oil powder to linseed oil. Stir thoroughly and allow to stand. Strain through muslin.

Blackboard coatings. Stain with black water stain, either proprietary or made with black aniline dye (see aniline dyes, water stain). Rub down and apply a second coat. Follow with the special proprietary blackboard preparation made for the purpose. Alternatively, thin drop-black with turpentine, and to 1 pint add a dessertspoonful of gold size; sprinkle in two heaped tablespoonfuls of fine carborundum powder. Stir thoroughly. Paint evenly over the surface, and give a second coat 12 hours or more later.

Bleaches

Oxalic acid. Useful for lightening the tone of wood locally, for bleaching stains which are too dark, and for taking out ink marks, etc.

Dissolve 1 oz. oxalic acid crystals in ½ pint hot water. Apply to work with rag. Several applications may be needed. Wipe over with borax, about 1 oz. to ½ gallon water. Wash with clear water and dry.

Oxalic acid is a poison and should be kept from the fingers. Remove all traces from the work, otherwise it may attack any subsequent finish.

For a more drastic bleach to produce the effect known as "bleached mahogany," etc., a powerful proprietary bleach is used on the bare wood. This will take the redness out of Honduras mahogany, leaving it almost white. It should be finished afterwards with white polish. The instructions supplied with the bleach should be followed. Cuban mahogany cannot be bleached successfully.

A mild bleach is a mixture of 1 part 0·880 ammonia and 5 parts water. When dry, follow with 100 vol. hydrogen peroxide diluted with 2 parts water.

Typical proprietary bleaches are *Blanchit*, *Ultra-bleach*, *Vitableach*, *Iso-bleach*, *Iaxa Bleach white*, etc. These are effective on the natural colour of the wood only, not on wood which has been stained.

Workshop recipes

Furniture creams

1. Melt together:
   - 6 parts carnauba wax.
   - 3½ parts japan wax.
   - 1½ parts paraffin wax.

Dissolve in about same quantity pure American turpentine to form paste. Stir well and add a little french chalk and ammonia.

2. Melt together:
   - 6 parts carnauba wax.
   - 3½ parts japan wax.
   - 1½ parts paraffin wax.

Dissolve in 12 parts pure American turpentine. Shred 3 parts white curd soap in 30 parts hot water. Add one mixture to the other whilst hot and stir well. Allow to cool. This cleans as well as polishes.

Limed oak

Put 2 lb. of unslaked lime in 3 quarts water and allow to cool off. Mix until it resembles paint and rub into the pores across the grain. When semi-dry wipe off surplus across the grain. Allow to dry. Rub down lightly with glasspaper and apply a coat of white french polish. Finish with white wax polish made with paraffin wax and turpentine to which is added zinc white powder. This increases the white deposit.

Alternatively, use a proprietary liming paste. This has merely to be rubbed into the grain. Being of a waxy nature the wood receives a dull eggshell gloss as the rubbing is continued. Liming paste is made with zinc white added to wax polish as described above.

Another method is to mix whiting with water to form a thick paste and rub well into grain. When dry rub across grain with brush to remove surplus whiting and follow with a coarse rag rubbed *with* the grain. A couple of rubbers of white french polish will give an eggshell shine, or white wax polish (see above) can be used.

Sometimes ordinary white oil undercoat paint is used, this being brushed into the grain and immediately wiped from the surface before setting begins.

Tool strop dressings.

For chisels, plane irons. etc. Fine emery powder mixed with lubricating oil. Smear over piece of soft leather. Alternatively, use *fine* valve grinding paste. Leather can be glued to a flat board.

Workshop recipes

For carving tools. As above for first stropping. For superfine edge use crocus powder mixed with vaseline. Pieces of wood with rounded edges to suit curve of tool can be prepared, leather being glued to the edges.

Non-slip recipes

Floor. Sprinkle plaster of paris on floor in front of bench.

Belt. To stop machine belt slip sprinkle ground rosin on belt.

or

Add linseed oil to ground rosin to make thick paste and heat. Apply to belt with stiff brush. Proprietary non-slip materials are also available.

Stoppings

Ready-made stopping can be obtained in sticks requiring to be melted; also proprietary stoppings. Plastic wood in tins can also be used, having the advantage of taking stain.

Beaumontage. A hard stopping for cabinet work. Mix equal parts beeswax and crushed rosin. Add a few flakes of brown or orange shellac. Heat in a tin and stir well together. Add powder colour to suit wood it is to match; vandyke brown for walnut and dark oak, or venetian red or red ochre for mahogany. Stir thoroughly and either keep in tin or pour out into the rounded corner of a tin lid to form into sticks. In the latter case heat a pointed iron and press the stopping against it so that the latter runs down into the hole. If kept in the tin the latter is heated and the stopping applied with a pointed matchstick.

Putty. For painted wood or rough deal work. It will not absorb stain. Add boiled linseed oil to dried crushed whiting and knead well. It can be coloured with venetian red powder to resemble mahogany or vandyke brown for dark oak.

Polisher's putty. For filling holes in deal and other light woods. Add white polish to whiting, mixing to the consistency of putty. Give the wood a coat of french polish before pressing in the mixture. This stopping will take spirit stain.

Cheap stopping. For cheap deal shelvings, fixtures, etc. It will absorb water stain. Mix plaster of paris with glue size. Press into the hole.

Other stoppings. Heel ball, brown or black, can be used, but it does not set very hard. Sealing wax of suitable colour is an alternative, but is brittle.

Lubricants

For drawers. Candlegrease rubbed on dry. Suitable for other working parts. Apply *after* polishing. Do not use oil.

For planes, saws, etc. Linseed oil (kept on a pad of cotton-wool). Russian tallow. Candlegrease.
Bits for dowelling should not be greased as it prevents glue from adhering.

Polish for turned work

Wax. Ordinary wax polish can be applied whilst wood is revolving in the lathe. After applying leave for several hours to allow the turps to evaporate before polishing. Carnauba wax gives a good gloss. Hold the lump wax against the revolving wood and move slowly across the work. Make a hard cloth rubber by tying a knot in fluffless cloth, press against the work, and more slowly along to spread wax evenly and burnish.

French polish. A special lathe polish can be obtained. It is thicker than normal polish and is applied with the lathe running at slow speed. It requires knack, as there is otherwise tendency to pull off polish and to form ribs. Two or three applications are needed. Finish with saliva from the mouth applied with a rag.

Varnish. This should be brush applied with the wood stationary. Use a rubbing variety and when thoroughly hard burnish with a motor-car polish applied with a rag, the work revolving at slowest speed.

Strippers

Proprietary strippers are generally used. The type should be selected according to the finish to be removed. A caustic type should be avoided when it is essential that the wood is not darkened.

Home strippers are:

1. Dissolve caustic potash in water and apply with rag on stick or a grass-hair brush. Leave surface coated. Scrape off old polish or paint, and wash down with clean water. Wipe over with vinegar.
This stripper is inclined to darken oak, mahogany, and other hardwoods.

2. 0·880 ammonia will strip old polish and varnish. Use scraper. Scrubbing brush is useful for carving. Wash down afterwards. Ammonia darkens most hardwoods, however. Avoid contact with the fingers as it is painful.

3. Household soda dissolved in hot water and used strong. Wash down afterwards. This will remove french polish. It has a slight darkening tendency.

4. Methylated spirits will soften french polish after a while, enabling it to be scraped off, but it takes a long time on very hard polish.

5. ½ lb. rock ammonia.   1 lb. washing soda.
   ½ lb. crude soft soap.   1 gallon hot water.
Leave to soak then scrape off. A scrubbing brush fed with pumice powder is sometimes useful. Wash down afterwards.

All traces of caustic or alkaline strippers must be removed as they may attack finishes subsequently applied.

Wood fillers

Most polish manufacturers supply fillers to suit their products. It is essential to use a filler compatible with the particular finish.

Other fillers are:

Plaster. Plaster of paris damped with water is rubbed into the grain. It is coloured with vandyke brown powder when used for dark oak or walnut, and with red ochre for mahogany. To apply dip a damp rag into the plaster and rub across the grain, wiping off the surplus. When thoroughly dry wipe over with raw linseed oil. This will kill the whiteness and enable any filler left on the surface to be wiped off in the form of a thick scum. Give two coats of french polish and allow to dry *before* applying filler.

Paste filler. To 1 lb. of crushed whiting add powder colour to take off the whiteness: red

Upholstery materials

ochre for mahogany, and vandyke brown for walnut and dark oak. Add turpentine to bring to a paste. Add 1 tablespoonful of gold size as a binder.

Another recipe is:
1 quart boiled linseed oil, 1 pint gold size or brown japan, 1 gill turpentine.
Mix together and add china clay or silex, little at a time, to form a stiff paste. Allow to stand twenty-four hours and thin with turpentine as required. It will not keep for much over a week.

Polish revivers

1. 1 part linseed oil.
   1 part vinegar.
   1 part methylated spirits.

2. Dissolve 1 oz. camphor in $\frac{1}{2}$ pint methylated spirits. Add $\frac{1}{2}$ pint vinegar, 1 oz. linseed oil, $\frac{1}{2}$ oz. butter of antimony.

3. 4 parts linseed oil.
   1 part terebine.
   12 parts vinegar.

Upholstery materials

Coil springs. Majority are copper-covered steel wire, but are sometimes black japanned or galvanised. Sizes range from 100 mm. to 250 mm. and in gauges 8 to 13. The lower the gauge number the stouter the wire.

Tension springs. Made in 12 mm. diameter (for seats) and 9 mm. diameter for backs. They are fixed at a tension of 40–50 mm. on a 450 mm. length. Made in several lengths.

Foamed latex rubber. This has largely replaced traditional stuffings and spring interiors. It is made in a wide variety of sizes and specially moulded shapes; also in sheets which can be cut to size. In addition there are chemical foams of the polyether and polyester groups. These are slower in regaining shape but are cheaper than foamed latex.

Spring units. Single, double, and triple spring units were originally made in various sizes and shapes.

Pocketed interiors. Used for cushion interiors. The coil springs are enclosed in calico or hessian. Both these and spring units have largely been replaced by chemical foams and latex rubber.

Webbing. Best grade is black and white twill weave of flax. Second qualities are mixtures of jute and cotton, or hemp. Cheaper grades are brown and are of jute. Usual width is 50 mm., but certain types are also available 53 mm. and 56 mm. The black and white grades are usually in 18 yard rolls and the brown jute qualities are put up in 33 m. pieces. Quality of the jute webbing is governed by weight: 10–11–12 or more lb. to the gross yardage.

Rubber webbing. This is highly resilient and has largely replaced twill. It is made in widths of 56 mm., 50 mm., 38 mm., and 19 mm. It is fixed either with tacks or special clips.

Hessian. Made in many weights and widths. Usual upholstery width is 1·82 m. Best quality is known as tarpaulin and is used mostly for covering over springs. Scrim is a more open type of hessian and the threads are rounded in section. It is used mostly for covering the first stuffing.

Stuffings. Horsehair is the most satisfactory of traditional stuffings. It is in various grades, the cheaper kinds consisting of short hair, or a mixture of horsehair and hog hair. Of the vegetable fibres coco fibre (brown in colour) is used for first stuffing, but has a tendency to become brittle and break up in time. Algerian fibre is either black or green, and of the two the former is more satisfactory. Both hair and the fibres can be obtained woven on to hessian to form stuffing pads. Latex rubber has largely replaced traditional stuffings.

Other stuffings include linsey wool (black wool) manufactured from rags, rugging which is similar but is made from jute rags and has not so much resiliency, and cotton flock which is a waste product from cotton.

Cotton waste or linters, felted together to form a type of wadding, and wadding, either sheet or pound, are used over hair or fibre stuffings before covering.

For cushions and bedding both feathers and kapok are used. The latter is a vegetable down from Java and the Dutch East Indies.

Twines. For sewing to webbing a fairly thick hemp twine is needed, but for stitching rolls and edges, running through, etc., a finer but equally strong twine is needed, known as stitching twine. Both kinds are usually put up in ½ lb. balls. For lashing the tops of springs together laid cord is used. The quality in all cases may vary in both materials and manufacture. A cheap twine may weigh heavier and so give less yardage to the ball.

Tacks. Sizes of tacks vary from 10·0 mm. to 16 mm. Improved tacks are of stouter build with larger heads, and these are used in 16 mm. size for webbing, and 10·0 mm. and 13 mm. for hessian. Fine tacks in the smaller sizes are used for various covers. Black japanned gimp pins are used for fixing gimps and trimmings, also covers in inconspicuous places such as the outside backs of chairs.

Glues

The following are the chief types. Those marked with an asterisk are used in special industries and are not normally available.

Animal	Fish	Casein	Cellulose
Resin	Polyvinyl acetate		Rubber based
*Vegetable	*Oilseed residue		*Blood albumin

Most modern glues are derived from one or other of these sources, and some are formed from combinations of them. Proprietary glues are given in italics under the various headings.

Animal glue. Under this heading is Scotch glue, which is obtained from the skins and bones of animals. It is obtainable in cakes which need to be broken up, though some makers supply it in powdered form, which quickens the preparation and enables the exact consistency to be more accurately judged. In its best form the skins of animals are used, when it is sometimes known as Salisbury glue. Prepared glues ready for immediate use can be obtained in tubes and tins which, according to grade, are applied hot or cold.

Croid Aero, Croid Universal; Fortil, Adams, Cox's, Calbar.

When properly used Scotch glue is extremely strong and in normal circumstances is durable. Furthermore, it is not liable to stain wood. As against this it is neither heat nor water proof, and it must be used hot. This last point means that arrangements have to be made to prevent the glue from chilling when it is applied to the wood. Cold application glue needs no heat except in Winter time when slight warming is necessary.

To make Scotch glue, break up the cakes and steep in water. Heat in a proper glue-pot (never with naked flame) and stir until thoroughly mixed. Make hot, but do not boil. Remove any scum from surface and test consistency by raising brush a few inches above pot. It should flow down freely without lumpiness yet without breaking up into drops. Heat the

Glues

work to be glued. For light woods add zinc white powder to the glue to prevent a dark glue line from showing.

Fish glue. In its best form this is made from isinglass, which is extracted from the bladder of the sturgeon. In lower quality glues the heads, skins, and cartilage of fish are used. It is handy for small jobs, but not for large woodwork because of its high cost. It has a somewhat objectionable smell. Usually sold in tubes. Its water resistance varies according to make.
Seccotine, Lepage's Liquid.

Casein glue. Skimmed milk is the basis of this glue. It is precipitated by the addition of a weak acid, and is marketed in the form of light-coloured powder. There are many proprietary forms of the glue and most of them are put up in small quantities so that it is suitable for home use. Casein is extremely strong and has the great advantage of being used cold (though hot-setting caseins are available). It is considerably more water-resistant than animal glue. A disadvantage is its liability to stain hardwoods, such as oak, mahogany, and other woods containing acid. Non-staining glues are available, but not all these are free from the trouble, and they are less water-resistant. One point to note is that joints must be cramped, since the glue is not sticky. They cannot be rubbed, since the glue is not sticky.
Casco, Croid Insol, Certus.

Cellulose-based glue. Put up in tubes and used for fixing plastics, metal inlay, ivory, etc., to wood. It is highly water-resistant and is free from staining. It is used cold.
Durofix.

Synthetic resin glue. This modern development is essentially the product of the chemist, and it has most of the advantages of other glues and is free from many of the snags. A drawback from the point of view of the small user is that some makes are liable to become rubbery if kept unused for more than three or four months, and are then useless.

To make a broad distinction, there are two general classes of glues: phenol-formaldehyde and urea-formaldehyde. Of these, some varieties of the former requires hot pressing in a thermostatically-controlled press. They are thus unsuitable for the small workshop, in which available cramping apparatus is comparatively primitive. Cold setting phenol-formaldehyde glues are widely used, but are critical in application and are therefore unsuitable also. Urea-formaldehydes, on the other hand, can be obtained for both hot and cold pressing, and it is the latter which will appeal to the small user, since it is used at normal temperature and needs no special apparatus.

These urea glues are put up in various forms, but generally they are in two parts: the glue proper and the hardener. The glue may be in the form of a treacle-like syrup or it may be a powder which requires to be mixed with water. The hardener is a transparent or coloured liquid, and has no adhesive value in itself; it is required purely for the reaction which takes place when it is brought into contact with the glue, causing the latter to solidify, quickly or slowly in accordance with its special type. Thus the glue, if used alone, can remain for a considerable time with little or no change, but when brought into contact with the hardener begins to react, with the result that it sets.

One method—which lends itself well to home workshop use—is the separate application system. The glue is applied to the one joining surface and the hardener to the other. The two are then brought together, when the process of hardening begins straightaway. In some brands the hardener must be still moist at the time of assembly. In other makes it is recommended that the hardener is allowed to dry out first. Sometimes it is permissible to apply both to the one piece. Generally the hardener is put on first. Another alternative with some makes and using a slow hardener is to mix the glue with the hardener and thus apply both together.

To overcome the drawback of the short life of the syrup form of glue, some makes are prepared as a powder which keeps indefinitely if kept sealed. This is mixed with water, when for all practical purposes it is the same as the syrup. The hardener is the same.

There are generally at least three hardeners to each kind of glue, and the difference between them is in the speed with which they cause the glue to set. Large work with many joints needs a slow hardener, whilst a job which has to be worked on soon is assembled with a quick hardener. For normal work a medium hardener is used. A point to be remembered is that heat speeds the setting. Yet another form of resin glue, also in powder form, has the hardener incorporated. It requires only to be mixed with water to be ready for immediate use.

Cascamite waterproof glue, Aerolite 300, Aerolite 306.

Polyvinyl acetate. A cold-setting resin glue in the form of a white and fairly thick liquid. It is used as it is from the container without a hardener. Many substances can be glued with it: wood, plastics, hardboard, fabrics, tiles, lino, rubber, etc. Joints can be rubbed or cramped, and the glue is free from staining, though glue may turn dark if used on some woods such as oak. The glue will keep for many months but should not be stored in a cold place. Generally the glue is liable to creep, that is, a heavy panel glued vertically may tend to slide slowly downwards.

Uni-bond, Casco P.V.A., Polystik, Lepage's, Bondfast, Redi-bond, Resin W one-way wet, Timbabond, Croid Fabrex.

Rubber-based adhesives. These are not generally used in ordinary wood assembling — in fact for some jobs they are impracticable. They have their uses for special work, however, and in bonding other materials to wood. In use the adhesive is applied to both surfaces and allowed to dry for 15–20 minutes. The two are then brought into contact when the bond is immediate. It follows then that great care has to be taken to position the work exactly because it is impossible to shift once the two are pressed home. Furniture repairers sometimes use it for items which would be difficult to cramp. By coating the surfaces and allowing to dry it is only necessary to press the two parts together when the bond is immediate. Of necessity it leaves a glue line because an appreciable glue thickness is bound to be left.

Its chief use, however, is in fixing plastic sheeting to wood frames or chipboard. No cramping is necessary but care has to be taken not to trap air in the middle of the panel, and to position exactly.

Evo Stik, Bostic C, Casco Super Contact, Unistik,

Vegetable glue. This glue is not of direct use to the ordinary woodworker, because it is not normally obtainable, its use being largely restricted to the manufacture of plywood. We include it here as a matter of interest, however. It is made from starch and has been in use from earliest times. It is a cheap glue and has the advantage that it can be used cold; furthermore, it remains in good working condition for a long period. On the other hand it has low water resistance, is slow setting, and is liable to stain certain woods.

Oilseed residue glue. In a sense this comes under the heading of vegetable glues, but it is usually classed separately as it is derived from soya beans, peanuts, or cotton seeds, and has come into use only within recent years. It is more in the nature of a casein glue. Like vegetable glue, it is not used in ordinary woodwork. It is in the manufacture of plywood that it is chiefly employed. Curiously enough it has not proved a success for hardwoods, plies made from Douglas fir and pine being its chief application. As its successful use requires the addition of a kali it is liable to stain hardwoods of an acid nature. An advantage is that it is water-resistant though not waterproof. It is not normally available.

Blood albumin glue. Here again is a glue which is used almost entirely in the plywood manufacturing trade and does not come into normal woodwork. It is derived from animal blood obtained from abattoirs. Used generally in conjunction with casein, it produces a water-resisting glue, but is liable to cause staining in some hardwoods. Heat is necessary in the pressing stage, this causing the albumin to coagulate, an essential feature of the process. It is not obtainable ready made.

Glues

Properties of glues

	Water resistance	Drying property	Hot or cold working	Micro-organism resistance	Staining liability
*Animal glue	Low	Slow	Hot	Low	Quite free
Fish glue	Low	Slow	Cold	Low	Quite free
Vegetable glue	Low	Slow	Cold	Low	Stains hard-woods
Oil-seed residue glue	Good	Medium	Cold	Low	Stains hard-woods
Blood albumin glue	Good	Rapid	Hot	Low	Stains hard-woods
Casein glue	Good	Medium	Cold (Hot also obtainable)	Medium	Stains hard-woods
Casein glue (non-stain)	Medium	Medium	Cold	Medium	Some brands free
Synthetic resin glue	High	Rapid or slow according to hardener	Hot or cold according to type	Complete	Generally free
Cellulose	High	Rapid	Cold	High	Free
Polyvinyl acetate	Low	Medium to fairly rapid	Cold	High	Free, though glue itself may be liable to darken on some woods
Rubber-based	Good	Rapid	Cold		Free

*Prepared forms of animal glue give varying degrees of water and heat resistance and of drying speed according to brand and grade.

Special glues

Brass inlay. Add a little plaster of paris to freshly-made Scotch glue; or add a table-spoonful of venice turpentine to a pint of Scotch glue. Keep well stirred when heating. A little garlic added to Scotch glue increases its strength for gluing metal inlays, and helps to keep it fresh. *Araldite epoxy glue* can be used.

Celluloid and ivory. Coat with paste made from celluloid dissolved in ether. Then use Scotch glue or Araldite epoxy glue.

Tortoiseshell. Use synthetic resin glue if possible. Failing this Salisbury glue is best. Scotch glue if used must be made up fresh for the job. Glue which has been repeatedly heated is useless. If a light colour is wanted add flake white to the glue. When a warm tone is needed mix rouge powder instead. This shows right through the transparent portions. Score the back with a fine file to give the glue a grip. For curved work steam the tortoise-shell to make it bend. Imitation tortoiseshell can be made pliable with acetic acid.

Baize and leather. Wallpaper paste made up to double strength. Cut baize ½ in. full all round to allow for shrinkage, and trim after twenty-four hours. Leather can be cut within an hour.

Rubber to wood. Use a rubber-based contact adhesive.

Plastics to wood. Use a rubber-based contact adhesive or one of the synthetic resins. Generally the surface of the plastic should be sanded to give a key to the glue.

Gilding materials

Gesso. Used in building up the foundation when water gilding. Also used in lacquer work. Cut up oddments of parchment, cover with water, and leave overnight. Gently simmer for several hours in a container with water jacket (glue-pot fashion). The water must never boil. Allow to chill when a thin jelly will be formed. If too thick the gesso will be brittle; too thin a jelly has no strength. As a test shake the jar (when cold). The jelly should fracture. Heat again and add superfine gilder's whiting until a creamy mixture is formed. A spot of linseed oil or tallow makes the gesso more manageable.

Gold leaf. Obtainable in books of 20 leaves. Two kinds are available: loose leaf and transfer. The former is used in water gilding. Transfer leaf is backed with thin paper and is used in oil gilding.

Gold size. A specially high grade is used for gilding. Two kinds are available: 2–4 hour and 18 hour. When there is time the slower is the more satisfactory. It is painted on with a small brush and allowed to become tacky before the gold leaf is applied.

Gilder's clay. Applied after gesso before the gold leaf is used when water gilding. It is moistened with water and painted on. Various colours such as brown, blue, and yellow are available.

Abrasive papers and cloths

There are many kinds and grades of abrasives used in various trades, and below are given those chiefly in use. It should be realised that the grading systems vary according to the abrasive, and, in order that a quick comparison can be made, we give in Chart A the comparative grades. Thus, taking No. 1½ glasspaper, the equivalent grade in garnet is 2/0, and 100 in aluminium oxide. We are indebted to English Abrasives Ltd., for much of the information contained on this and the following pages.

Glasspaper. Used chiefly for the hand smoothing of wood. Abrasive grains are of crushed glass. Supplied in sheets 11 in. by 9 in.
   Grades: 2/0 or Flour, 0, 1, 1½, F2, M2, S2, 2½, 3.

As general guide use M2 for preliminary smoothing followed by No. 1 or 1½. For delicate woods use No. 0, and when rotary movement is needed on fine woods (as in burr walnut) use Flour to finish.
   Made in close coat only.*

Glass cloth. This is preferred in some trades. Grades are as in glasspaper, and size of sheets is 11 in. by 9 in.
   Made in close coat only.*

Garnet paper. Used for both hand and machine sanding. Supplied in sheets 11 in. by 9 in., and in rolls, belts, discs. The abrasive grains are the natural crushed garnet stone.
   Grades (in sheets): 8/0, 7/0, 6/0, 5/0, 4/0, 3/0, 2/0, 0, ½, 1, 1½, 2.
   Grades (in rolls): 5/0, 4/0, 3/0, 2/0, 0, ½, 1, 1½, 2, 2½, 3, 3½.
   As a comparison 2 is of same coarseness as 1½ glasspaper.
   Made in both open and close coat.*

Aluminium oxide paper. Used chiefly for machine sanding, but can also be obtained

Abrasive papers and cloths

in sheets size 11 in. by 9 in. for hand work. The grit is very hard. Aluminium oxide (derived from bauxite) is the abrasive used.

   Grades: 9/0, 8/0, 7/0, 6/0, 5/0, 4/0, 3/0, 2/0, 0, ½, 1, 1½, 2, 2½, 3.

Made in both open and close coat.*

2/0 aluminium oxide corresponds with 1½ glasspaper.

Aluminium oxide cloth.   Made only in rolls and discs for machine work.

   Grades: 400 (very fine) up to 24.

Made in both open and close coat.*

Flint paper.   This has only a limited use in woodwork. Flint is a natural product and is not so hard as garnet, aluminium oxide, or glass. One or two woodworking trades use it, but generally it is used more in other industries. Flint paper is made in sheets 11 in. by 9 in.

   Grades: 150 up to 3-24 coarse.

As a comparison 100 Flint corresponds with 1½ glasspaper.

Made in close coat only.*

Silicon carbide paper.   This is seldom used for machine sanding except sometimes in floor surfacing. But chief users are the leather and metal-working industries. It is made in sheets 11 in. by 9 in. and in rolls and discs. The grit is exceptionally hard and durable.

Silicon carbide cloth.   Made in sheets 11 in. by 9 in. and in rolls, close coat only.*
Grades (in sheets and rolls): 320, 280, 240, 220, 180, 150, 120, 100, 80, 60, 50, 40, 36, 30, 24.

Chart A. — Comparative grades of abrasive papers and cloth

Glass-paper Glass cloth	Garnet Aluminium oxide (woodworking)	Flint paper sheets	Aluminium oxide Silicon carbide (metal-working)	Emery cloth
			400	
	9/0		320	
	8/0		280	
	7/0		240	
	6/0		220	0
00 or Flour				
0	5/0		180	
1	3/0	120	120	F
1½	2/0	100	100	
F2				1½
M2			60	2
—	—	—	—	
S2				2½
2½	1½	1½	40	3
3	2	2	36	½
—	2½	2½	30	4
—	3	3	24	4½

Waterproof silicon carbide sheets.   In sheets 11 in. by 9 in.
Grades: 400, 320, 280, 240, 220, 180, 150, 120, 100, 80, 60.

   The grades of these waterproof papers are the same as the corresponding gluebond papers.

Open and close coat. These terms refer to the spacing of grains on the paper. In the "open" there are spaces between the grains, making the paper less liable to choke. It is therefore used more on softwoods and resinous woods and surfaces liable to cause choking. In the "close" the grains are close together, making them suitable for hardwoods.

Screws

Screw hole sizes. Two distinct sizes of holes are needed when screwing—a thread and a clearance hole. The former is the hole into which the screw bites its way, and should be smaller than the over-all diameter of the shank. The clearance hole should be a trifle fuller than the shank diameter.

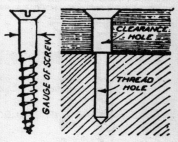

Finding the gauge of a screw. If you are uncertain of the gauge of a screw this simple method will give the exact answer in a few moments. Measure across the head of the screw, counting the measurement in sixteenths of an inch; double this number and subtract two. This is the gauge.

For example: a No. 10 screw (independent of length) will measure ¾ in. or ⁱ²⁄₁₆ in. This multiplied by two is 1½ in.; less two is ¹⁰⁄₁₆ in., or No. 10.

Holes required when screwing.

Gauge	Clearance hole		Thread hole	
	inch decimal size	inch fractions	inch decimal size	inch fractions
0	0·060	¹⁄₁₆	0·035	—
1	0·075	⁵⁄₆₄	0·040	—
2	0·095	³⁄₃₂	0·050	—
3	0·095	³⁄₃₂	0·058	¹⁄₁₆
4	0·110	⁷⁄₆₄	0·065	¹⁄₁₆
5	0·125	⅛	0·075	⁵⁄₆₄
6	0·140	⁹⁄₆₄	0·085	³⁄₃₂
7	0·155	⁵⁄₃₂	0·090	³⁄₃₂
8	0·175	¹¹⁄₆₄	0·095	³⁄₃₂
9	0·185	³⁄₁₆	0·102	⅛
10	0·200	¹³⁄₆₄	0·110	⁷⁄₆₄
12	0·220	⁷⁄₃₂	0·140	⁹⁄₆₄

Exact drill sizes need not be followed closely, and in any case are variable in accordance with the kind of wood being screwed. Hard woods generally need a larger thread hole than a soft wood.

Screws

At the time of going to press it is uncertain how screws may be classified under the metric system. It is quite possible that existing gauges will be retained and lengths given eventually in mm.

Metals. The chief kinds are mild steel (iron) and brass, but in addition screws are made in copper, gunmetal, aluminium, and in a variety of finishes, such as Berlin blacked, galvanised, tinned, nickel-plated, electro-brassed, antique brassed, antique copper, electro-coppered, copper-oxydised, electro-silvered, and blued. The range of sizes is not so great in these fancy finishes.

Types. Countersunk head, raised head, and round head are the types mostly used. Size is taken from the position shown by arrows. Raised heads are frequently used with screw cups, which increase gripping area and give a neater appearance. Phillips head also available. This has centre recess rather than slot.

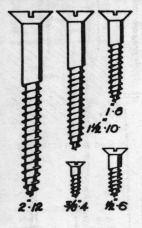

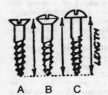

A. Countersunk head.
B. Raised head.
C. Round head.

Twinfast screws have parallel twin threads of steep pitch so that the screw is driven twice as far for the same number of turns. They are used mostly in industry.

Sizes. Screws are classified by length and gauge. Illustration above shows from where length is taken. Gauge is the diameter of the shank and is the same in all lengths of screw. For instance, a 1-in. 9-gauge screw would have the same diameter and size of head as a 2-in. 9-gauge screw. Gauges range from 0000 to 50, but those from 4 up to 12 are most commonly used. Diagram shows five common gauges in actual size. Order screws this way: "2 hundred 1¼-in. 9s, countersunk, iron." It is always cheaper to buy by the hundred than dozen.

Nails

There are dozens of different kinds of nails made for special purposes, and their names vary not only with particular trades but also in different localities. Those shown here are generally representative, but there are additional nails made for special purposes. Nails are mostly sold by weight. All the illustrations are in full size so that the relative stoutness of the types can be judged. At the time of going to press it is uncertain whether nails will be altered to exact metric lengths. We have therefore retained Imperial measurements. To find the metric equivalents turn to the conversion tables on page 125.

A. Lost-head wire nail. Joinery. Head makes only small hole, easily punched in.
Sizes 1½–4 in. (2-in. shown).
Finishes: Bright mild steel, galvanised.

B. Oval wire nail. Joinery. Not so liable to split grain as round nails.
Sizes ½–6 in. (2-in. shown).
Finishes: Bright mild steel, galvanised.

C. French or wire nail. Carpentry, case-making, etc.
Sizes ½–6 in. (2-in. shown).
Finishes: Bright mild steel, galvanised.

D. Cut floor brad. Fixing floorboards. Not liable to split grain.
Sizes 1½–3 in. (2-in. shown).
Finish: Black iron.
  Cut joiner's brad. Same shape, but slightly lighter
Sizes ½–3 in.
Finish: Black iron.

E. Cut clasp nail. General-purpose carpentry nail. Grips strongly.
Sizes ¾–8 in. (2-in. shown).
Finish: Black iron.

F. Panel pin. Cabinet work, joinery, etc. Fine gauge, small head.
Sizes ⅝–2 in. (1½-in. shown).
Finishes: Bright mild steel, brass, coppered.

G. Veneer pin. Veneers, small mouldings, etc.
Sizes ⅝–1½ in. (¾-in. shown).
Finish: Bright mild steel.
  Finishing pin. Similar, but finer.
Sizes ¼–¾ in.
Finish: Bright mild steel.

H. Cut tack. Upholstery, etc.
Sizes ¼–1¼ in. (⅝-in. shown).
Finishes: Blued or black iron, tinned, galvanised, copper.
  Improved tack. As above, but with larger head.

I. Wire clout nail. Roofing felt, chair webbing, canvas, etc.
Sizes ¾–3 in. (1-in. shown).
Finishes: Bright mild steel, galvanised.
  Cut clout nail. Sharp point stays in when pressed with fingers.
Sizes ¾–3 in.
Finish: Black iron.

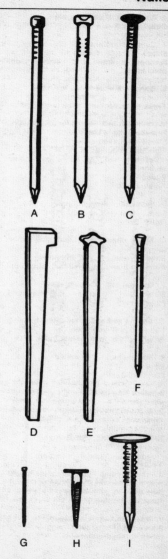

Nails

J. Wire tack. Upholstery, etc.
Sizes $\frac{1}{2}$–1 in. ($\frac{3}{8}$-in. shown).

K. Covered tack or stud. Fixing gimp.
Sizes $\frac{3}{8}$–$\frac{1}{2}$ in. ($\frac{1}{2}$-in. shown).
Finishes: Leather and leather cloth covered.

L. Sprig. Picture backs, lino, etc.
Sizes $\frac{1}{2}$–$\frac{3}{4}$ in. ($\frac{5}{8}$-in. shown).
Finish: Black iron.

M. Wire lath nail. Laths for plaster work. Fine shank, large head.
Sizes $\frac{3}{4}$–1$\frac{1}{4}$ in. (1-in. shown).
Finishes: Galvanised..

Cut lath nail. As above but square section.
Sizes $\frac{7}{8}$–1$\frac{1}{4}$ in.
Finish: Black.

N. Brass pin. Fixing fittings.
Sizes $\frac{1}{4}$–1$\frac{1}{4}$ in. ($\frac{1}{2}$-in. shown).
Finish: Brass.

O. Brass chair nail. Decorative upholstery work.
Sizes (of head) $\frac{1}{8}$–$\frac{1}{2}$ in. ($\frac{3}{8}$-in. shown).
Finishes: Brass, antique (dull), black iron.

P. Drugget nail. Carpets, etc.
Sizes, head $\frac{3}{8}$–$\frac{3}{4}$ in.; pin $\frac{3}{4}$–2 in. ($\frac{3}{4}$-in. shown).
Finish: Brass.

Q. Square nail and rove. Boat building.
Sizes $\frac{1}{2}$–6 in. (2-in. shown).
Finishes: Copper, mild steel, galvanised.

R. Roofing nail. Corrugated iron roofs.
Sizes 2$\frac{1}{2}$ in.
Finish: Mild steel.

S. Stack pipe nail. Fixing pipes to brickwork, etc.
Sizes 2–6 in. (2$\frac{1}{2}$-in. shown).
Finish: Iron.

T. Deck head nail. Shipbuilding.
Sizes 1$\frac{1}{2}$–8 in. (2-in. shown).
Finishes: Galvanised iron, copper.

U. Needle point. Veneers, small mouldings, etc. Headless and tempered.
Sizes 1$\frac{1}{8}$–1$\frac{1}{2}$ in. (1$\frac{1}{8}$-in. shown)
Finish: Bright steel.

V. Wire gimp pin. Upholstery.
Sizes $\frac{3}{8}$–$\frac{3}{4}$ in. ($\frac{3}{4}$-in. shown).
Finish: Brass and blacked.

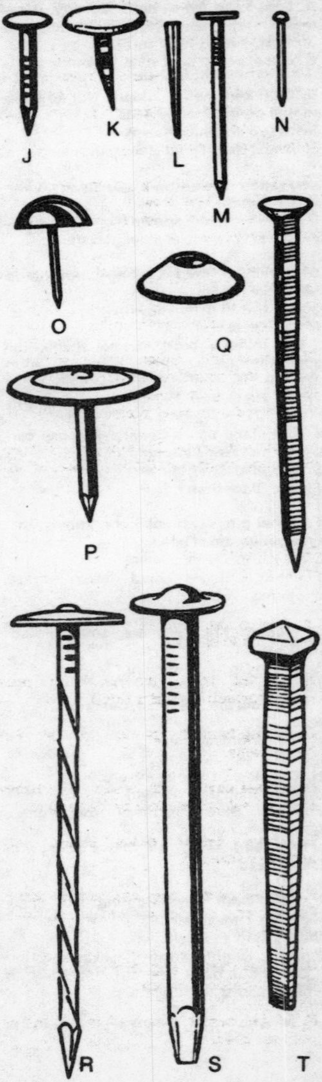

Cut gimp pin. As above but square section. Long, thin, sharp point.
Finish: Black iron.

W. Corrugated fastener. Crude joints in cheap work.
Sizes, depth $\frac{1}{4}$–$\frac{7}{8}$ in.; length $\frac{7}{8}$–$1\frac{1}{2}$ in. ($1\frac{1}{2}$ in. by $\frac{3}{8}$ in. shown).
Finish: Bright steel.

X. Staple. Upholstery springs, wire, etc.
Sizes $\frac{1}{2}$–4 in. (1-in. shown).
Finishes: Bright mild steel, galvanised, coppered.

Y. Escutcheon pin. Metal fittings to wood.
Sizes $\frac{3}{8}$–$1\frac{1}{2}$ in. ($\frac{3}{4}$ in.-shown).
Finishes: Brass, bright iron.

Z. Screw nail. Sheet metal to wood. Heads, flat, countersunk, or round.
Sizes $\frac{1}{2}$–2 in. ($\frac{5}{8}$-in. shown).
Finishes: Bright steel, plated.

Diamond point. Generally sherardised. For fixing hardboard. Common size is $\frac{3}{4}$ in.

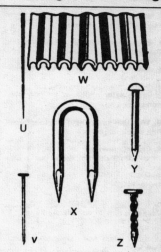

Castors

A. Minicastor. Rubber tyred ball castor. Screw-plate fixing.

B. Hooded wheel castor. With wide wheel covered by plastic hood.

C. Spring-loaded piano castor. For heavy items.

D. Swivel castor with brake. For heavy duty. Wheel can be fixed by foot brake.

E. Wheel castor, plate fixing. Ball-bearing swivelling.

F. Spring castor, peg and socket fixing. For wagons, etc. for easy movement over carpets, etc.

G. Wheel castor, peg and socket fixing. General-purpose castor.

H. Wheel castor, screw plate. General-purpose castor.

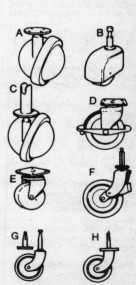

Metal fittings

I. Spring wagon castor. Large wheel travels easily over carpets.

J. Round socket castor. For table and chair legs.

K. Square socket castor. Fixing over square legs.

L. Ball castor. With screw or plate fixing.

M. Floor glide. Spreads load over wide area.

N. Slipper glide. A glide which also swivels for easy movement.

O. Glide. For chairs, tables, etc. Glides easily over the floor.

Stays

A. Wardrobe stay. To limit opening of a door.

B. Casement stay. To hold casement in various positions.

C. Pneumatic stay. Primarily for record players. Lid can be dropped and will close silently.

D. Cocktail cabinet stay. Opens fall and lid simultaneously

E. Friction stay. Holds lid in a required position.

F. Door stay. Holds door open in any position.

G. Bureau hinge and stay. Supports fall in down position.

H. Quadrant stay. For lid for which straight stay would be impracticable.

46 **I. Rule-joint stay.** Used for lids and hinged seats. Made right- and left-hand.

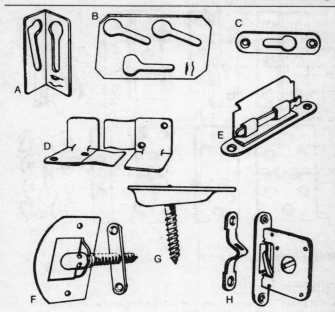

Knock-down fittings

There are many types of fittings, some of them made specially for and used only by manufacturers. Those below show some of the fittings commonly available.

A. Corner plates. For drawing pieces together at right angles. Made right- and left-hand.

B. Screw plate. For pulling together parts in same plane.

C. Single fixing plate. Acts in same way as slot screw.

D. Self locking fittings. Parts have simply to slide one within the other.

E. Leg fitting. One part fixed beneath top, other engages in slots in leg. Insertion of metal wedges locks parts.

F. Bolt and plate. Slotted screw engages with plate. Bolt tightened with tommy bar.

G. Table-leg plate. Legs are screwed in at correct slope.

H. Cam action. Turning slot draws parts together by cam or hook action.

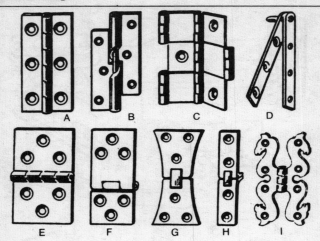

Metal fittings

Hinges

A. Butt hinges. For cupboard and room doors, boxes, etc. Require letting equally into both door and carcase, or wholly into either.

B. Rising butts. For lifting room door clear of carpet. Made right- and left-hand. To tell hand required stand outside door. If hinges are to the right right-hand hinges are required, and *vice versa*.

C. Screen hinges. Enable folds of screen to hinge both ways. To be let into both joining edges. Distance between pin centres must equal or be not less than timber thickness.

D. Centre hinges. For letting into top and bottom of door. Plates let into both door and cabinet. Lower hinge should have raised seating or washer around pin to prevent binding. Made straight as shown, or cranked to throw door clear of cabinet.

E. Back flap hinges. Used chiefly for bureau falls. To be let into both joining parts.

F. Table leaf hinges. For leaf tables having rule joint. Countersunk on reverse side so that knuckle is recessed into wood. One flap is longer to bridge across joint. Short side is fixed to top, and long side to leaf.

G. Counter hinges. Double-jointed hinge enabling entire hinge to be flush without projecting knuckle. Let into face of counter and flap.

H. Card table hinges. Double-jointed hinge leaving a flush surface when opened. Let into face of top and flap. Type for letting into edges is also available.

I. Butterfly hinges. Decorative hinge screwed straight to face of door and framing.

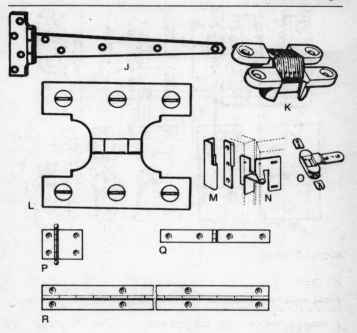

J. Cross-garnet hinges. For ledged doors, etc. Screwed on face.

K. Soss hinges. Let into the edge of the door. Are entirely concealed when door is closed.

L. Parliament hinge. For a room door to fold back flat to the wall to clear architrave, skirting, etc. Knuckle projects from door face slightly more than half the greatest projection of the architrave.

M. Lift-off hinge. Door pivoted from outer corner enabling it to fold back flat through 270 deg.

N. Pivot hinge. When opened through 90 deg. the throw-off action keeps the door in line with the cabinet side.

O. Onyx invisible hinge. Fitted in various ways and invisible from outside.

P. Clockcase hinge. Used when door stands out from face of case, hence one wide flange.

Q. Strap hinge. Used when hinge has to be fixed to a narrow edge.

R. Piano strip hinge. Fixed to wide falls similar to lid of piano.

Metal fittings

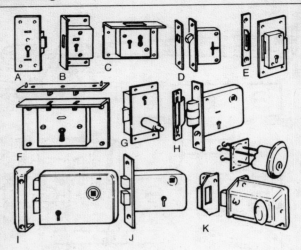

Locks

A. Straight cupboard lock. For door fitting between ends. Requires no letting in. Bolt shoots both ways.

B. Cut cupboard lock. For door fitting between ends. Needs cutting into door. Made R- and L-hand.

C. Cut drawer lock. Recessed inside drawer front.

D. Sliding door lock. To be recessed into edge of door.

E. Link-plate lock. For door closing over face of ends. Bolt shoots R- or L-hand.

F. Cut box lock. Lock is cut into box and plate into lid.

G. Wardrobe push latch. Screwed to rear of door, button projecting through hole.

H. Roller mortise latch. Let into edge of door. Opened from outside with key, and by revolving knob at inside.

I. Rim lock. Screwed inside door. End plate is recessed; also box staple. May be R- or L-hand, or reversible.

J. Mortise lock. Recessed entirely into edge of door. The latch may be reversible.

K. Cylinder latch. Key cylinder requires to be recessed. Usually with locking device on bolt.

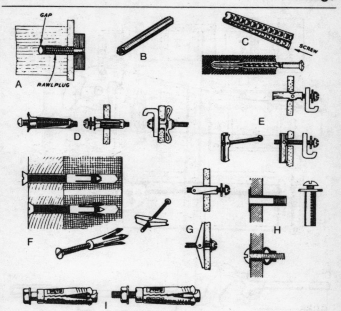

Fixings

A. Rawlplug. A fibre tube for inserting into a hole drilled in brick or similar wall.

B. Expandet screw anchor and Woden wall plug. A rubber plastic tube to be inserted into a hole.

C. Alex screwplug. An aluminium plug for inserting in a hole.

D. Rawlanchor. For thin walls. When the bolt is tightened the flexible arms bend outwards.

E. Rawlplug gravity toggle. For a cavity or thin wall. The arm drops down after being passed through the wall.

F. Recco wallplug. For brick and similar walls using a Whitworth bolt rather than a wood screw.

G. Rawlplug spring toggle. For thin or cavity walls. After being passed through a hole in the wall the sprung arms fly outwards.

H. Philplug Taylor nut and rawlnut. A hard rubber bush with metal insert threaded for metal bolt. Suitable for walls liable to crumble.

I. Rawlbolt and Philplug expandabolt. Suitable for fixing into concrete.

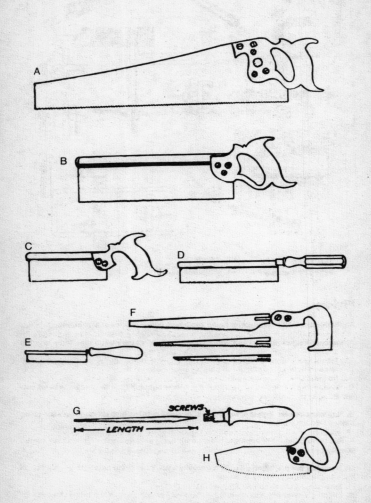

A

B

C   D

F

E

G   SCREWS

LENGTH

H

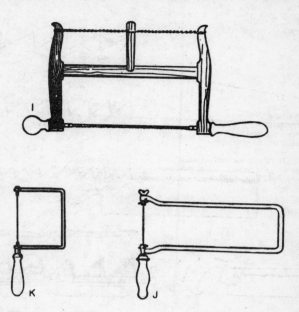

Tools

A. Handsaws. *Rip saw* cutting *with* the grain 0·61 m.–0·71 m. 3–6 points. *Cross-cut saw* sawing across the grain, but can also be used for ripping. 0·56 m.–0·71 m. 5–10 points. *Panel saw* fine sawing and large joints. 0·45 m.–0·61 m. 7–12 points.

B. Tenon saw. General bench work and larger joints. 0·3 m.–0·4 m. 12–14 points.

C. Dovetail saw. Fine work and small joints. 0·20 m.–0·25 m. 16 points.

D. Bead saw. Small work generally. 0·10 m.–0·30 m. 16 points.

E. Light back saw. Finest sawing, small dovetails. 0·10 m.–0·20 m. 24–32 points.

F. Nest of saws. Internal cuts and flat shapes. 0·25 m., 0·32 m., 0·45 m. blades.

G. Keyhole saw. Small internal straight and curved cuts. Blade 0·27 m.–0·40 m.

H. Flooring saw. Cutting existing flooring.

I. Bow saw. Cutting curves. Blades 0·20 m.–0·40 m.

J. Fret saw. Fine shapes in thin wood. Frame 0·30 m.–0·50 m.

K. Coping saw. Cutting shapes and scribing. Blade 0·15 m.

Tools

Tooth shape
A. Ripsaw teeth.
B. Cross-cut teeth.
C. Tenon and dovetail teeth.

Pitch. The angle the front of each tooth makes with the general line of the teeth. It varies from 75 deg. to 90 deg.

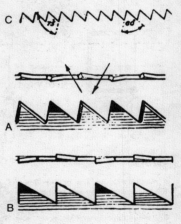

Bevel. The angle at which the file is held in relation to the saw when sharpening. A. For cross-cut, tenon and dovetail saws it varies from 45 deg. to 60 deg. B. For the ripsaw it is 90 deg.

Tooth size. The number of points per inch including those at both ends. The words 'per inch' are to be dropped in future.

(9 POINTS PER INCH)

Set. The extent to which the teeth are bent over alternately each side. Set should extend only halfway down the tooth except for small teeth.

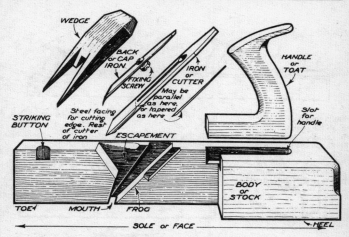

Parts of the wooden jack plane

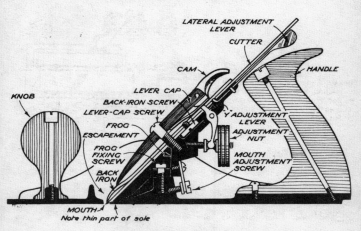

Parts of the adjustable metal plane

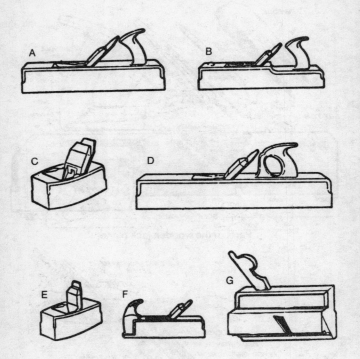

Wood planes

A. Jack. Rougher preparatory work. 0·35 m.–0·43 m., cutter widths 50 mm.–56·50 mm.

B. Technical jack. Lighter than the normal Jack plane and with recessed handle. 0·35 m. Cutter 50 mm.

C. Smoothing. Final cleaning up. Cutter 50 mm.–56 mm.

D. Trying. Joints and large work. 0·56 m.–0·61 m. Cutter 63 mm.

E. Toothing. To give key for glue and take out inequalities when veneering. Cutter 50 mm.

F. Roughing. Really rough work. Cutter 38 mm.

56 **G. Moulding.** Various patterns. English held at angle, Continental upright.

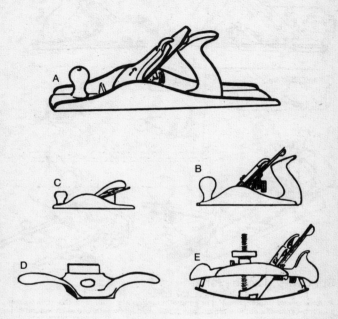

Metal planes

A. Jack. General bench work, short joints, etc. 0·35 m., cutter 50 mm., 0·38 m., cutter 60 mm.
  Fore. Joints and large work. 0·45 m., cutter 60 mm.
  Jointer. Long joints, etc. 0·56 m., cutter 60 mm.

B. Smoothing. Cleaning up and general bench work. 0·24 m., cutter 44 mm., 0·25 mm., cutter 50 mm., 0·27 m., cutter 60 mm.

C. Block. Small work generally 150 mm.–180 mm., cutter 34 mm.–40 mm. Low angle (12 deg.) 152 mm., cutter 34 mm.

D. Scraper, handled. Cutter 69 mm.

E. Compass. Circular work, concave and convex, cutter 44 mm.

Tools

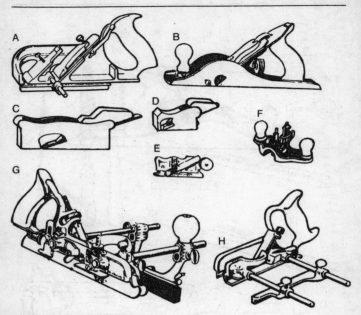

Special-purpose planes

A. Rebate and fillister plane. For general rebating. With spur for cross-grain working, additional bullnose cutter position, and fence. Also made with two arms to hold latter. Cutter width 38 mm.

B. Carriage rebate plane. For wide rebates. Has double iron. 228 mm. and 330 mm., cutter 53 mm.

C. Shoulder plane. End grain trimming and fine work generally. Cutter widths 16 mm., 19 mm., 25 mm., 31 mm., 38 mm. Also made with detachable front and with bullnose.

D. Bullnose plane. For small rebates. Works close to a corner. Cutter widths 10 mm. to 28 mm.

E. Side rebate plane. For trimming groove sides. Has detachable nose.

F. Router plane. Levelling or working grooves. Made with both closed and open mouth (latter shown). With 3 cutters and fence.

G. Multi-plane. Grooving, rebating, beading. It works at its best for grooving. Eleven cutters $\frac{1}{8}$ in. to $\frac{7}{8}$ in., or 3 mm. up to 22 mm., also beading, matching and sash cutters (There are also various other grooving planes.)

H. Small plough plane. Cutters 4 mm., 6 mm., 9 mm.; and 12 mm. Also $\frac{1}{8}$ in., $\frac{7}{32}$ in., and 58 $\frac{1}{4}$ in.

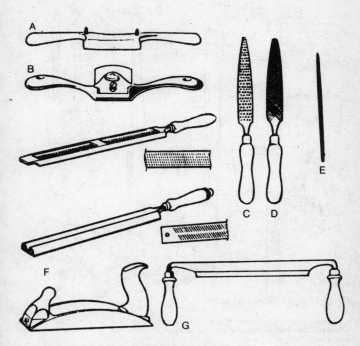

Spokeshaves, rasps, files, etc.

A. Spokeshave, wood.   Trimming shaped edges. Cutter widths various, average 50 mm.

B. Spokeshave, metal.   Trimming shaped edges. Made flat face for convex edges and round face for concave shapes. With or without cutter adjustment. Cutter width 44 mm. and 53 mm.

C. Rasp.   Preliminary rough shaping. Half-round section 150 mm. to 250 mm.

D. File, half-round.   Removes coarse rasp marks on shaped edges. 150 mm. to 250 mm.

E. Rat tail file.   For small acute hollow curves 150 mm. to 200 mm.

F. Shapers and open files.   Non-clogging tool for wood and abrasive substances such as chipboard, etc. Cuts rapidly. Obtainable in flat file form or in shape of a plane. Also coarse and fine.

G. Draw knife.   Rapidly reducing wide boards, rounding squares, etc. 250 mm. good average size.

59

Tools

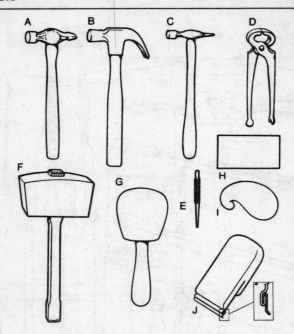

Hammers etc.

A. Warrington hammer. Sizes 00–12. Useful weight about 11 oz.

B. Claw hammer. Carpentry. Sizes 7–30 oz. Useful weight 1 lb. 10 oz.

C. Pattern maker's hammer. Small nails. 3–6 oz.

D. Pincers, tower. 152 mm.–200 mm.

E. Punch or set. Square for cut brads, round for wire nails. Hollow point is most satisfactory.

F. Mallet. Carpentry and cabinet work. 100 mm.–180 mm.

G. Carver's mallet. Lignum vitae preferably, 200 mm.–220 mm.

H. Scraper. 100 mm.–150 mm. About 1·20 mm. thick.

I. Curved scraper. For hollow surfaces. About 120 mm., 1·20 mm. thick.

J. Skarsten scraper. Cleaning up. Also with long handle for floorboards and toothing cutter.

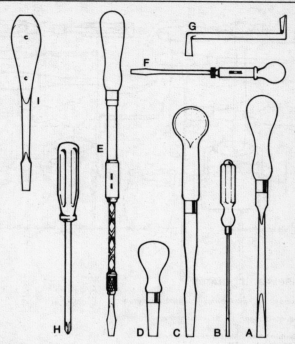

Screwdrivers

A. Cabinet.   General-purpose tool, blades 75–305 mm.

B. Electrician's.   Invaluable for small screws. Various lengths.

C. London.   Strong pattern, blade 75–400 mm.

D. Plane iron or pocket pattern.   Stubby type 35–65 mm. blade.

E. Spiral-ratchet.   Pump action for rapid turning of screws. Can also be locked rigidly. Closed lengths 190 mm.–500 mm.

F. Ratchet.   Specially useful for hanging doors. Grip on handle remains unchanged, leaving left hand free. Blade lengths 50 mm.–200 mm.

G. Cranked.   For screws in position which normal screwdriver cannot reach. About 125 mm.

H. Phillips.   For screws with Phillips head. Blade 75 mm.–200 mm.

I. Engineer's.   Can be struck with hammer for difficult screws. 75 mm.–250 mm.

Tools

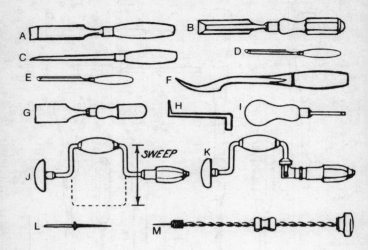

Chisels and gouges

A. Firmer. Fairly stoutly-built for general bench work.

B. Bevelled edge. Light tool for paring and dovetails.

C. Sash-mortise. Mortise chisel of medium build.

D. Firmer gouge. Bevel ground at outside, for general use.

E. Scribing gouge. For scribing mouldings, etc. Bevel ground inside.

F. Swan-neck. For cutting recess for mortise lock.

G. Sash pocket. Used when cutting pocket in sash window frame.

H. Drawer-lock chisel. Used in confined space when cutting recess for drawer lock.

Boring tools

J. Simple brace. Sweep 125 mm.–300 mm.

K. Ratchet brace. Can work through part sweep only. Sweep as above.

I. Bradawl. Screw holes, etc. Various sizes.

L. Birdcage awl. As above but square section. Not liable to split wood.

M. Archimedean drill. For extra fine holes.

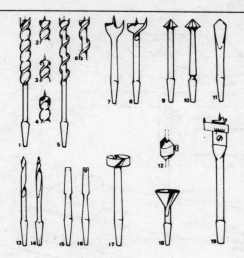

Bits

1–6. Twist or auger bits. Deep, clean boring such as dowelling.
1. Jennings. 2. Scotch nose. 3. Gedge. 4. Solid nose. 5. Irwin. 6. Irwin single cutter.
No. 2 has no spurs and is for rough work.
Nos. 3 and 4 are specially useful for angle boring since there are no projecting spurs to foul the wood.
No. 6 is for green or stringy wood.

7, 8. Centre bits. For shallow holes. In no. 8 the thread draws the bit into the wood.

9. Snailhorn countersink. Recessing screw heads in wood.

10. Rose countersink. For brass.

11. Flat-head countersink. For iron.

12. Broughton countersink. For attaching to drill bit.

13. Wood drill bit. Used mostly for screw holes.

14. Cobra bit. For screw holes. Quick boring but liable to split the wood.

15. Screwdriver bit. Quick-driving and when great leverage is needed.

16. Forked screwdriver bit. For tightening slotted nuts.

17. Forstner bit. Bores smooth holes with little centre recess as it is guided by its rim.

18. Dowel trimmer. For chamfering end of dowel.

19. Expansion bit. Bores shallow holes of varying size within its capacity. Two sizes available; 13 mm.–38 mm. and 22 mm.–76 mm. Extra cutters are available up to 152 mm. but are suitable for soft woods only.

Tools

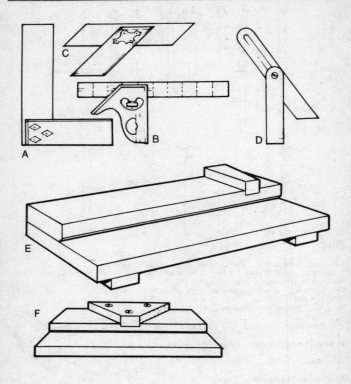

Squares

A. Try square. Blade 150 mm.–300 mm.

B. Engineer's square. In addition to normal use can be used for rebates, etc. Useful size 300 mm.

C. Mitre square. Testing 45 deg. mitres. Blade size 200 mm.–300 mm.

D. Sliding bevel. Marking odd angles. Blade 200 mm.–300 mm.

Appliances

E. Shooting board. Butt joints and end trimming. About 0·450 m. to 1·80 m.

F. Mitre shooting board. Trimming mitres. About 0·45 m.

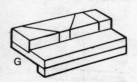

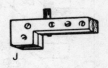

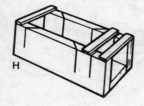

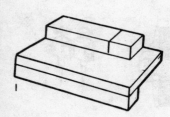

G. Mitre block. Cutting small mitres. About 0.25 m.

H. Mitre box. Cutting large mitres. To take up to 100 mm.

I. Bench hook. Holding wood whilst sawing. About 230 mm.

J. Scratch stock. Working mouldings and inlay grooves. About 125 mm.

K. Mitre templet. Mitreing stuck mouldings. About 100 mm.

L. Veneering hammer. Pressing down veneer. Blade about 120 mm.

Tools

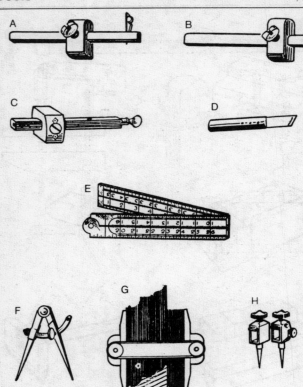

Marking and testing tools

A. Cutting gauge.   Marking or cutting any direction of grain.

B. Marking gauge.   Marking *with* the grain. Metal patterns also available.

C. Mortise gauge.   Marking mortise and tenon joints.

D. Marking knife.   For setting out joints, etc.

E. Rule.   Made for both metric and Imperial measurements.

F. Dividers.   For stepping out odd measurements and scribing circles, 125 mm.–300 mm.

G. Moulding templet.   Enables section of moulding to be ascertained. Various sizes.

H. Trammel heads.   For fixing over wood bar for marking out. Some have pencil socket.

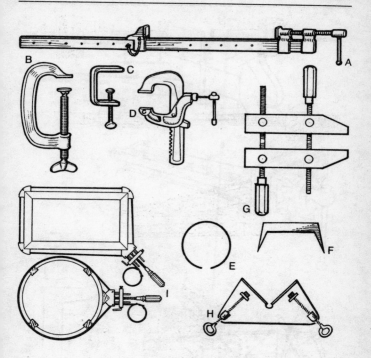

Cramps

A. Sash cramp. 0·60 m.–1·50 m. Also T sections, 0·60 m.–2·10 m. Lengthening bars are obtainable for both.

B. G cramp. To take 50 mm.–305 mm

C. Thumbscrew. 50 mm.–100 mm.

D. Carver cramp. 150 mm.–300 mm.

E. Spring cramp. Light cramping, specially repair work.

F. Joiner's dog. Holding edge joints while glue sets.

G. Handscrew. Wood chops, metal screws. Average 300 mm. chops.

H. Mitre cramp. Grips mitres while nailing, several patterns available.

I. Band cramp. For square or circular work.

Tools

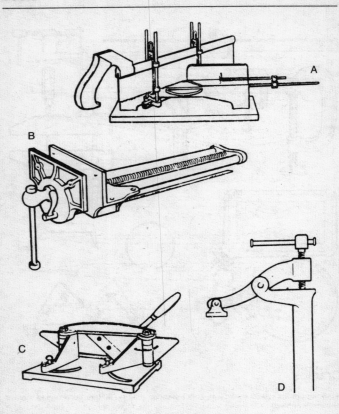

Appliances

A. Mitre cutter. Cross-cuts up to 45°, each side of a square 90° angle. Various sizes for cutting up to 50 mm., 100 mm., and 150 mm. Stop for repetition cutting provided.

B. Bence vice. Various patterns and sizes opening from 113 mm., to 380 mm. Some are of plain screw type, others quick-grip with lever as shown to disengage the nut. A third kind can be released by turning backwards but automatically takes up on turning clockwise.

C. Mitre trimmer. Trims end grain, either of square cuts or of mitres. Can be adjusted from 45° to 90°.

D. Bench holdfast. Grips work on the bench, the shaft being passed through a hole in the bench top. Pillar sizes 250 mm. to 450 mm.

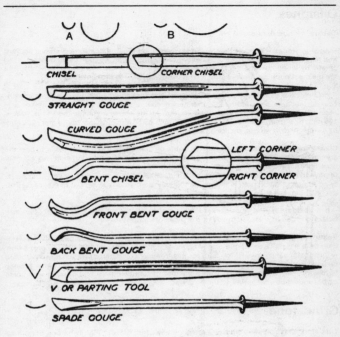

Carving tools

These are generally known by width of blade and a number which denotes the curvature, though the system varies with different makers. One common rule is that all tools of the same number have the same type of curve. Thus, all No. 9 tools are semi-circular in section regardless of width. Sizes range from $\frac{1}{16}$ in. up to 1 in. and are obtainable with or without handles. Parting tools are available in varying angles ranging from about 40 degrees up to 90 degrees.

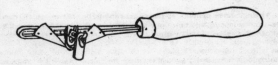

Tectool. For working either curved or straight grooves. Cuts in either direction to suit grain. Various cutter widths provided, but they can be staggered to cut extra wide grooves. 69

Oilstones, grindstones, grinding wheels

Oilstones

Two main kinds, natural and artificial.

Natural stones. — *Washita* cuts well and gives good finish. Occasionally stones go hard and lose their cut. *Arkansas.* High quality stone giving superfine edge but expensive. Used chiefly by wood carvers, dental mechanics, and so on. There are other types but these are the most popular. *Turkey stone.* — Gives good quality edge for finishing.

Artificial stones. — These have advantage of constant quality. Are made in three grades: *coarse, medium,* and *fine,* also combination *coarse and fine.* Well-known makes are: *India, Carborundum, Aloxite, Unirundum,* etc. All the above are made in various sizes — 125 mm. by 50 mm., 150 mm. by 50 mm., 200 mm. by 50 mm., 250 mm. by 50 mm., 200 mm. by 45 mm. Also in various sectioned slips.

Cleaning a gummed stone. If an unsuitable oil is used on a stone it is liable to become gummed, thus choking the pores and robbing it of its cut. A method of cleaning which is usually effective is to scrub it with a stiff brush dipped in kerosene oil or petrol. This will remove the old oil and dirt. If it does not yield rapidly to this, soak it for twenty-four hours or so in petrol, then brush it. If this fails the only alternative is to send it to the makers for a refinishing operation.

It is seldom that the woodworker finds a stone cuts too rapidly, but the cut of an artificial stone can be retarded by soaking in a pan of hot vaseline.

Resurfacing a stone. If a natural stone becomes out of shape it can be levelled by rubbing on a flat piece of marble or paving stone, using silver sand and water to give a bite. Artificial stones are usually too hard for this treatment, and carborundum powder should be used instead of sand. Some workers prefer to rub down on a flat piece of close-grained hardwood, this being dressed with a mixture of lubricating oil and paraffin with some carborundum powder sprinkled on the surface. Use a fine-grade powder for fine stones.

Grindstones

York stone and Yorkshire Blue Grit are generally used: latter is slightly harder. Should be used wet, but not allowed to stand in water. Does not draw temper of steel. Various sizes from about 150 mm. diam. by 37·9 mm. up to 0·90 m. by 100 mm.

Grinding wheels

Made in various grits — *emery, aluminous oxide,* and *corundum* under different trade names. Sizes range from 50 mm. by 6·3 mm. to about 300 mm. by 37·0 mm. Used dry. Care needed for woodworking tools owing to liability to draw temper.

Sharpening tools

Planes. A trying-plane or smoothing-plane cutter should be only very slightly curved, and have a really pronounced curve for a roughing plane. Shoulder, bullnose, and rebate plane cutters must be both straight and square.

The grinding angle of cutters is in the region of 25 deg., and the honing angle 30 deg. An exception is the cabinet-maker's plane, which has a high pitch of about 50 deg. This usually needs to have its cutter honed at about 35 deg., as otherwise it is liable to chatter. The cutter is held with the bevel flat on the stone (Fig. 1), the hands raised a trifle so that only the edge touches the stone, and worked back and forth. This rubbing turns up a burr at the back, which can be detected by drawing the thumb across the edge. This is an indication that it is sharp, though it does not reveal the quality of the edge or whether it is

Fig. 1.—Sharpening cutter.

Fig. 2.—Turning back burr.

free from gashes. To detect the latter, look at the edge in a good light—gashes will show up as little spots of light.

Turn back the burr by reversing the cutter flat on the stone and rubbing once or twice as in Fig. 2. To get rid of the burr draw the edge across the corner of a block of wood. A slight roughness will be left, but this can be got rid of by stropping on a piece of leather dressed with fine emery and oil. When the honed bevel becomes wide the cutter should be reground.

Scraper plane. After initial grinding and honing a keen edge at about 45 deg. turn the edge with a ticketer or gouge. Fix cutter edge uppermost in vice and place ticketer flat on bevel. Raise the handle slightly and rub along the edge with fair pressure. Increase tilt and make another stroke. Finally bring ticketer to within 15 deg. of the horizontal and again rub down.

Toothing plane cutter is sharpened similarly to bench plane cutter, except that edge is straight and no attempt is made to remove the burr.

Scraper. This tool cuts by virtue of an edge which is turned back. A ticketer or a gouge is used for turning the edge, which must be really sharp and square to start with.

Hold the scraper in the vice, and rub edges down with a flat file until square and sharp. Finish off on the oilstone. Afterwards rub each side flat on the stone. The edges have now to be turned. Place scraper flat on bench, its edge standing in a short way from the edges, and hold down with the fingers. Moisten the ticketer

Sharpening scraper plane cutter.

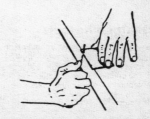

Fig. 1.—Turning the edge.   71

Sharpening tools

or gouge in the mouth and draw it along flat on the scraper once or twice in each direction, as in Fig. 2. If the gouge is used, make sure that it clears the fingers of the left hand.

Now hold the scraper so that it overhangs the edge of the bench about ⅛ in. Holding the ticketer at a slight angle, draw it along the edge once in each direction with firm pressure. Treat all four edges alike. The angle at which the ticketer is held is about 80 deg. As the edges become dulled they can be restored two or three times by flatting, as in Fig. 2, and turning back afresh. When this ceases to be effective it is necessary to file and hone afresh.

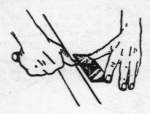

Fig. 2. — Flatting the sides.

Turning tools

Gouges. There are no separate grinding and honing angles. For bowl turning this should be not less than 45 deg., and edge should be straight, as at (D), Fig. 1. For work between centres, angle can be less and a nose given to the tool (B).

Chisel. This should have equal flat bevels at both sides. combined angle about 43 deg. If chisel is long-cornered, angle measured across side should be about 60–70 deg.

Fig. 1. — Details of turning tools.

Scraper tools. Worn-out files ground to shape, Fig. 2. Serrations are ground off on one side and the edge ground at about 75 deg. For some woods grinding is at lower angle, and after honing the edge is turned with ticketer.

Fig. 2. — Various shapes of scraping tools.

Chisels. These are ground at about 20–25 deg., but honing angle is in the region of 30 deg. for paring chisels. Those for chopping might be sharpened at about 35 deg. This honing makes a second bevel, and when this becomes wide it is necessary to have chisel ground afresh.

Sharpening tools

Hold chisel with bevel flat on the stone and raise the hands slightly. This gives an angle of 30 deg. Rub back and forth as in Fig. 1, varying the position on the stone. This turns up a burr which can be detected by drawing the thumb across the edge at the back. Reverse the chisel flat on the stone and rub once or twice, so bending back the burr (Fig. 2). Get rid of burr by drawing the edge across the corner of a waste piece of wood. Finish by stropping on leather dressed with fine emery and oil.

Gouges. Sharpen firmer gouge on oilstone with rocking movement, and finish inside with slip held flat. Scribing gouges are sharpened inside with slip and finished outside on oilstone. Tool is held flat and given a rocking movement.

Fig. 1.—Sharpening chisel.

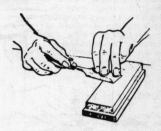

Fig. 2.—Turning back burr.

Fig. 1.—Rubbing outside bevel on oilstone.

Fig. 2—Sharpening inside bevel.

Carving tools. These are sharpened with a bevel on both sides, that on the inside being about one quarter of that outside. Use a fine-grade stone. For the outside bevel use a rocking movement as Fig. 1. For the inside bevel an oilstone slip of slightly less curvature than the gouge is needed, Fig. 2. Finish by stropping both sides.

For the V tool use oilstone slip of triangular section. It will be found that a sort of hook is formed at the apex. To remove this, rub the outside corner of the bevel on the stone.

Strops can be made of wood covered with leather and dressed with oil and crocus powder.

Sharpening tools

Filing centre bit.

Fig. 1. — Metal spokeshave cutter.

Fig. 2. — How wood spokeshave cutter is held.

Centre bit. Nicker is filed at the inside only. It should have greater protection than the cutter, but less than the centre point. It should either be rounded or sloped so that it cuts, not scratches. The cutter is filed as shown, and underside should have slight clearance.

Twist bits. Use file with safe edge to avoid damaging thread. Sharpen nickers on the inside only.

Half-twist bits. Use rat-tail file in alignment with line of the twist. It is obvious which side of the hollow cuts the wood and has to be kept sharp.

Spoon and shell bits. Cutting end is of spoon form which limits the number of times it can be sharpened. Rub with a rocking movement on an oilstone.

Shell bit is similar but end is not spooned. Either a fine file or the oilstone can be used. Bevel is flat, but the centre is higher than the sides.

Countersinks. Snail type touched up with flat file or oilstone slip rubbed in the hollow.

Forstner bits. Sharpen flange at inside with edge of a three-cornered file having its serrations ground away. Remove the burr by rubbing flat on the oilstone.

Expansion bit. Use fine file or oilstone for both cutters, retaining bevel.

Bradawl. Round type is filed and finished on oilstone. Square section type has usually to be ground.

Spokeshave. Metal spokeshave cutter is gripped in holder, as Fig. 1. This is simply a block of wood with a kerf in it. Sharpen as plane iron. Wood spokeshave cutter has projecting tangs. It is gripped in a handscrew, as in Fig. 2, or in the vice, and oilstone slip rubbed across the bevel. Do not remove the burr at the front as this helps the tool in its cut.

Draw knife. It is held so that its edge slightly overhangs the edge of the bench, and the oilstone is taken across it at slight angle. Retain existing bevel. Turn back burr by rubbing stone *flat* on reverse side.

Axe and adze. Hold axe so that edge overhangs bench, and work oilstone across bevel with a slight tendency towards edge.
   Sharpen adze with oilstone, holding tool on bench so that edge just overhangs. Hold stone flat on the bevel and press rather towards the edge.

Light machines

Circular saw. Obtainable both as a bench machine and on a stand. Generally known by largest size saw machine will take. For small workshop 170 mm. to 250 mm. most suitable. Either table or saw should have vertical adjustment to enable grooving and rebating to be done. Tilting table or saw also desirable for bevel cuts. A riving knife should be fitted to prevent wood from binding on the saw. Fence for ripping is needed, and table should have groove to take an adjustable mitre gauge for cross-cutting and mitreing. Guard is also essential.

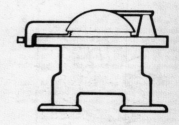

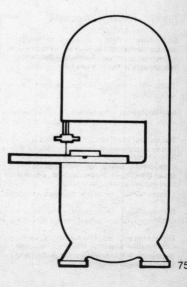

Bandsaw. Used chiefly for cutting external shapes. Can be used for straight cuts but is not so satisfactory as circular saw. May have either two or three wheels. Latter gives greater clearance for wood. Upper wheel must have tracking adjustment to keep saw in centre of rim; also vertical adjustment to enable saws of varying size to be fitted and to enable tension to be varied. Guides and thrust wheel should be fitted. Table should tilt, and have groove to take mitre block.

Light machines

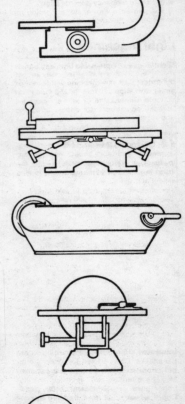

Jig saw. Used almost solely for internal cuts. Machine may be of rocker-arm type; the blade may be connected to a plastic band making the whole continuous, or it may be of the spring-return type. The latter type must be firmly bolted down because vibration is pronounced. Tilting table is an advantage. Hold-down foot is also useful.

Planer. Size of planer is reckoned by length of cutters, varying from 100 mm. up to 0·75 m. Tilting fence and guard should be fitted, and both tables adjustable. Rebating table is an advantage. Surfacer or jointer planes surface or edge straight and square.

Thicknesser brings wood to an even thickness, and any number of pieces can be brought to the same thickness. Many surfacers can now be fitted with a thicknessing attachment.

Belt sander. Path of abrasive is straight, and can therefore be used for smoothing as well as trimming. Tracking adjustment is necessary to keep belt true.

Disc sander. Size known by diameter of disc. Used chiefly for trimming rather than smoothing. Table should tilt and have groove to take mitre gauge.

Combination sander. Has disc, belt, and bobbin sanders, enabling small flat and curved parts to be sanded.

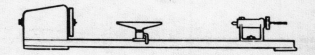

Wood turning lathe. Size known by maximum distance between centres and height of centres above bed (4 in. lathe will turn work of just under 8 in. maximum diameter). Heavy headstock and bearings are desirable.

Circular saw data

Peripheral speed. The rate at which the teeth are moving. Theoretically this should be in the region of 3,000 m. per minute (but see note below).

Revolutions per minute of saw (r.p.m.). This should vary with the diameter of the saw, and is based on the peripheral speed (3,000 m. per minute). It is found thus

$$\frac{\text{Peripheral speed}}{\text{Diameter of saw} \times 3 \cdot 143}$$

Example — Saw diameter, 0·30 m.

$$\frac{3,000}{0 \cdot 30 \times 3 \cdot 143}$$

$$= \text{say } 3,180 \text{ r.p.m.}$$

Note — The above can be accepted for saws of about ·30 mm. diam. and upwards. Smaller saws seldom achieve the optimum, however, often because the bearings are not suitable for the high speed, and also because many machines have various attachments which require a lower speed. In practice, saws running at lower speeds cut perfectly well if kept sharp. As an example, the theoretical optimum speed of a 0·20 m. saw is about 4,770 r.p.m. In fact, most saws of this size run somewhere between 2,000 and 2,500 r.p.m. They will cut quite well at 1,000 r.p.m. if sharp.

Theoretical optimum speeds are approx:

0·18 m. diam. 5,300 r.p.m.	0·30 m. diam. 3,180 r.p.m.
0·20 m. diam. 4,770 r.p.m.	0·35 m. diam. 2,700 r.p.m.
0·25 m. diam. 3,950 r.p.m.	0·40 m. diam. 2,380 r.p.m.

As noted above, the 0·18 m.–0·25 m. saws can run from 2,000–2,500 r.p.m.

Pulley sizes. When no pulleys are fitted to either saw or motor, the ratio between the speeds of the two must be found. The motor r.p.m. is usually marked on it.

Circular saw data

Example – Motor r.p.m. 1,450
Required Saw r.p.m. 3,000

$$\frac{1,450}{3,000}$$

$$= \frac{29}{60}, \text{ say } \tfrac{1}{2}$$

Therefore motor requires pulley twice size of saw pulley, giving saw speed of 2,900 r.p.m.

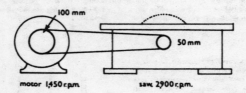

motor 1,450 r.p.m.   saw 2900 r.p.m.

It is a help to remember that when the saw is required to have a higher r.p.m. than the motor it must have the smaller pulley.

To find size of saw (driven) pulley:

$$\frac{\text{r.p.m. motor} \times \text{diameter motor pulley}}{\text{r.p.m. saw}}$$

Example – Motor r.p.m. 1,450; motor pulley 100 mm.; r.p.m. saw 2,500

$$\frac{1,450 \times 100}{2,500}$$

say 60 mm.

To find size of motor (driving) pulley:

$$\frac{\text{Saw r.p.m. required} \times \text{diameter saw pulley}}{\text{r.p.m. motor}}$$

Example – Saw r.p.m. 2,200: saw pulley 100 mm.: motor r.p.m. 1,500

$$\frac{2,200 \times 100}{1,500}$$

say 150 mm. diam

78

Power of motor. The motor should be powerful enough to drive the saw when cutting to maximum capacity. Except for the lightest work it should not be less than $\frac{1}{3}$ h.p. The following are generally recommended:

Saw diam.	H.P. motor	Saw diam.	H.P. motor
0·18 m.	$\frac{1}{4}-\frac{1}{3}$	0·35 m.	2–3 •
0·20 m.	$\frac{1}{2}-\frac{3}{4}$	0·40 m.	3–4$\frac{1}{2}$
0·23 m.	$\frac{1}{2}-1$	0·45 m.	5
0·25 m.	$\frac{1}{2}-1$	0·50 m.	7
0·30 m.	$1\frac{1}{2}-2$		

The lower figure is for comparatively thin wood or softwood. For tough hardwood, especially thick stuff, the more powerful motor should be used.

Saw gauges. This is the thickness of the metal. The following are generally recommended:

Saw diam.	Stubbs Gauge	Saw diam.	Stubbs Gauge
0·15 m.	21	0·30 m.	18
0·20 m.	20	0·40 m.	17
0·25 m.	19	0·45 m.	16

Special saws

A. Hollow-ground, dimension, or planer saw. Plate is thinner at centre and teeth have no set. Teeth are usually peg type (see below). Saw cuts cleanly leaving finish almost equal to that of a planer.

B. Swage saw. Flat on one side, tapers towards rim on the other. Teeth have usually more set on tapered side than in the flat. Centre thickness stiffens the plate, and thin edge reduces saw kerf. Used generally for cutting narrow strips which bend away from saw without binding.

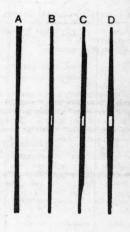

C. Ground-off saw. Gives very stiff plate but narrow kerf. Similar uses to the swage saws, but for still narrower pieces. For thin wood only.

D. Taper saw. Similar uses to swage and ground-off saws.

All these three saws (**B, C,** and **D**) should have minimum projection above saw table. Should not be used for general ripping or cross-cutting, but for special purposes only.

Saw teeth.

A. Peg teeth. Used for cross-cutting but now largely superseded by type at B.

B. Cross-cut teeth. Front edges are radial to saw.

C. Cross-cut teeth. Note that front edges leans back slightly. The high back to the teeth makes for strength.

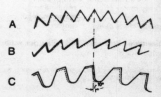

79

Transmission

D. Rip-saw teeth for softwood. Note the pronounced hook formed by the angle of the front.

E. Rip-saw teeth for hardwood. Similar to D but with less hook, making a stronger tooth.

F. Combination teeth. With mostly cross-cut teeth, but with raker teeth at every fifth or seventh position.

G. Tungsten toothed saw. Widely used today. Made in a wide variety of types and sizes and of particular value for abrasive materials such as chipboard.

Pitch of saw is distance between each point.

Transmission

The methods most suitable for small machines are the flat belt and the V belt. The former should have the driving side of the belt below so that the sag occurs at the top, thus increasing the arc of contact and lessening any liability to slip. The leather should be dressed monthly to keep it in good condition. Single ply flat belting will transmit the following loads approximately:

25 mm. wide, up to 1 h.p.	65 mm. wide, up to 3 h.p.
45 mm. wide, up to 1·5 h.p.	90 mm. wide, up to 6 h.p.

V belts are specially useful when pulley centres are close. Arc of contact should be not less than 120 degrees to avoid slip. This generally means that ratio between pulleys should not be greater than 1 : 7. If a greater ratio is essential, a countershaft should be installed. A V belt should never need any dressing. A point to realize is that a belt at low speed will not transmit as much power as when at high speed. Fortunately, most woodworking machines run at fair speed.

Pulley calculations. When making any calculations it is useful to remember that:

When the motor (driving) pulley is larger than the machine (driven) pulley the machine will run faster than the motor, and vice versa. Equal pulleys give same speed in both.

Thus, keep the following in mind:

Large motor pulley
and } = Machine runs faster than motor
Small machine pulley

Small motor pulley
and } = Machine runs slower than motor.
Large machine pulley

When no pulleys are fitted. Find the ratio between the motor r.p.m. and the required machine r.p.m.

Example – Motor r.p.m. 1,500: Machine r.p.m. 2,000

$$1,500 : 2,000 = 3 : 4$$

As machine must run faster than motor it must have the smaller pulley,

$$\therefore \text{ pulleys are in ratio, motor 4; machine 3}$$

Note that any sizes giving same ratio could be used, as 80 mm. : 60 mm., 120 mm. : 90 mm., 160 mm. : 120 mm., 240 mm. : 180 mm., etc.

To find motor pulley size

$$\frac{\text{Required machine r.p.m.} \times \text{Diameter machine pulley}}{\text{R.p.m. motor}}$$

Example — Motor r.p.m. 1,500; required machine r.p.m. 4,000; machine pulley 50 mm.

$$\frac{4,000 \times 50}{1,500}$$

133·3, say 130 mm. motor pulley.

To find machine pulley size

$$\frac{\text{R.p.m. motor} \times \text{Diameter motor pulley}}{\text{Required r.p.m. machine}}$$

Example — Motor r.p.m. 3,000; required machine r.p.m. 2,000; motor pulley 100 mm.

$$\frac{3,000 \times 100}{2,000}$$

150 mm. = machine pulley.

V belt pulley calculations. As the speeds of woodworking machines are not usually critical it is usual to take the outside diameter of V pulleys when calculating speeds. This, however, does not give exact speeds, and when this is required it is necessary to ascertain the *Pitch Circle Diameter* of both pulleys to be used. This (known as P.C.D.) is found as follows:

P.C.D. = Outside diameter of V belt pulley, minus thickness of belt, plus 1·6 mm.

Example — 100 mm. diam. V belt pulley 1,500 r.p.m. driving 200 mm. diam. V belt pulley. Thickness of belt 9·5 mm.

100 mm. − 9·5 mm. + 1·6 mm. = 92·1 mm. P.C.D. of 100 mm. pulley
200 mm. − 9·5 mm. + 1·6 mm. = 192·1 mm. P.C.D. of 200 mm. pulley

Now apply normal calculation:

$$\frac{1,500 \times 92 \cdot 1}{192 \cdot 1}$$

= 719·15 approx., say 720 r.p.m.

If the outside diameter of the pulleys had been used the answer would have been 750 r.p.m.

Line and counter-shafts. These are often used as a matter of practical convenience, where more than one machine is driven from one motor, or when the ratio between driving and driven pulleys is very great.

When one line shaft has to drive several machines, the individual speeds of which vary, it is sometimes convenient to fit pulleys of equal size to both motor and line shaft. In this case, since line shaft and motor revolve at equal speeds, all calculations for other pulleys can be made as for directly from motor to machine, each being calculated according to 81

Transmission

the speed required. If, however, all machines have to revolve at a speed well in excess of the motor, it is often convenient to step up the line shaft r.p.m. by fitting to it a smaller pulley than to the motor. A simple calculation gives the resulting line shaft r.p.m., and all pulley sizes for individual machines are worked out from this.

Example — A motor r.p.m. of 1,500 is required to drive a saw with 50 mm. pulley at 2,500 r.p.m.; a planer with 65 mm. pulley at 4,000 r.p.m.; and a sander with 75 mm. pulley at 2,000 r.p.m.

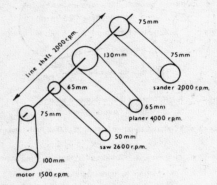

The slowest machine is the sander and the line shaft might be stepped up to this speed. The ratio is:

$$\text{Motor } 1,500 = 3$$
$$\text{Line shaft } 2,000 = 4$$

As the line shaft has to turn the faster it has the smaller pulley

therefore motor pulley 100 mm.
line shaft pulley 75 mm.

$$\frac{1,500 \times 100}{75} = 2,000 \text{ r.p.m. line shaft}$$

Saw with 50 mm. pulley to revolve at 2,500 r.p.m.

$$\frac{\text{Saw r.p.m.} \times \text{diameter saw pulley}}{\text{R.p.m. line shaft}}$$

$$\frac{2,500 \times 50}{2,000} = 62 \cdot 5 \text{ mm., say } 65 \cdot 0 \text{ mm.}$$

say 65 mm. diam. line shaft pulley to connect with saw, giving 2,600 r.p.m.

Planer with 65 mm. pulley to revolve at 4,000 r.p.m.

$$\frac{4,000 \times 65}{2,000} = 130 \text{ mm. diam. shaft pulley to connect with planer.}$$

Sander with 75 mm. pulley to revolve at 2,000 r.p.m.
Since both line shaft and sander have same r.p.m., no calculation is necessary. They
82 have pulleys of equal size.

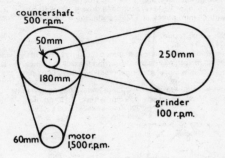

Example—Motor of 1,500 r.p.m. with 60 mm. pulley to drive grindstone at 100 r.p.m. Ratio is 1 : 15.

As this would give too small an arc of contact in the driving pulley a counter-shaft is used. The 15 can be substituted by any two numbers which, multiplied together, equal it. Thus 3 and 5.

As motor has 60 mm. pulley it should connect with 180 mm. counter-shaft driven pulley. Counter-shaft driving pulley can be 50 mm. connecting with 250 mm. grinder pulley, or any other sizes which have a ratio of 1 : 5. Resulting grinder speed is 100 r.p.m.

Machine speeds

Although optimum speeds have been found by experience and calculation, a wide variation is practicable for woodworking machines, providing they are sharp. The following are a guide showing the speeds at which to aim:

Circular saw. See notes under circular saw.

Band saw.

Diam. of wheel	R.p.m.
300 mm.	950
450 mm.	950
600 mm.	800
750 mm.	750

Many small band saws run at considerably lower speed than the optimum.

Jig saw. 600–1,700 r.p.m. (one stroke per revolution).

Planer. Cutter block of 75 mm. and less, 4,000–6,000 r.p.m.

Lathe.

Diameter of wood being turned	R.p.m. of work	Diameter of wood being turned	R.p.m. of work
25 mm.	3,000	200 mm.	650
50 mm.	2,500	300 mm.	570
75 mm.	1,500	450 mm.	300
125 mm.	1,000	600 mm.	250

Spindle. 4,000–8,000 r.p.m. High speed gives best results, but small machines seldom achieve this.

Motors

Sander.   Disc type:

Diameter	R.p.m.
250 mm.	600–2,500
400 mm.	900–1,000
600 mm.	400–570
750 mm.	200–340

Small spindle type – 2,000 r.p.m.
Drum type – 900–1,500 r.p.m.
Belt type – 300 m.–900 m. per minute (calculate according to size of cylinder).
Drill.   650–3,500 r.p.m. (often variable). The larger the drill the slower the speed.
Mortising machine (hollow chisel and auger type).   2,500–3,000 r.p.m.
Router.   18,000–27,000 r.p.m.
Grinders.   Dry type. Peripheral speed not more than 1,500 m. per minute.

                Average speeds: 150 mm. wheel – 3,100 r.p.m.
                                 200 mm. wheel – 2,300 r.p.m.
                                 250 mm. wheel – 1,900 r.p.m.

      Wet type. 450 mm. – 95 r.p.m.
                 600 mm. – 70 r.p.m.

Power of motor for machines

Circular saw.   (See under circular saw.)
Band saw.

Diam. of wheel	H.P. motor
300 mm.	0·33
450 mm.	0·5
600 mm.	1·5
750 mm.	3·0

Jig saw.   Small machines – 0·5 h.p.
Planer.

Length of cutter block	H.P. motor
100 mm.	0·33–0·5
150 mm.	0·5–1·0
225 mm.	1·0–1·5
300 mm.	2·0

Lathe.   100 mm. (height of centres above bed) – 0·33–0·5 h.p.
Spindle.   Small machines 0·33–0·5 h.p., or for larger cutters 0·75–1·0 h.p.
Sanders.   Disc type:

Diameter	H.P. motor
250 mm.	0·5–1·0
400 mm.	1·0
600 mm.	3·0
750 mm.	4·0

      Small spindle type 0·33–0·5 h.p.

      Single drum type 150 mm. diam. 0·75 h.p.
                            250 mm. diam. 1·5 h.p.

      Belt type 100 mm. width 0·33–0·5 h.p.
               150 mm. width 0·5–0·75 h.p.

Drills.   For boring up to 25 mm. holes 0·25–0·33 h.p.
Mortising machine.   For chisels up to 12 mm. 0·33 h.p.
Router.   0·25–3·0 h.p. according to size.
Grinder.   Dry stone – 150–200 mm. diam. – 0·25–0·5 h.p.
                    250 mm. diam. – 1·0 h.p.
      Wet stone – 450 mm. diam. – 0·5 h.p.
                    600 mm. diam. – 0·66 h.p.

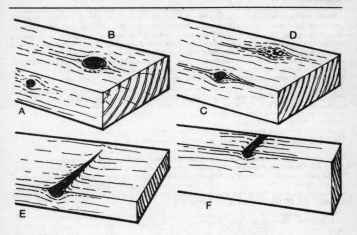

Knots

A. Edge knot. Round or oval knot occurring at the edge of a board.

B. Face knot. As above but on the face rather than the edge.

C. Arris knot. One occurring at the arris or sharp corner of timber.

D. Knot cluster. Several small knots in a group and having the wood fibres flowing around the whole.

E. Splay or spike knot. One which is exposed by a cut parallel with its length.

F. Margin knot. A knot cut parallel with its length and showing at the arris as part of a circle.

G. Loose knot. One which is not tightly held in place and may be pushed out. A tight or sound knot is firm.

H. Pin knot. One no more than 0·65 mm. diam.

I. Dead knot. One not joined throughout its length to the surrounding wood.

Moisture content

Cut timber is never bone dry except in exceptional circumstances. It loses or gains moisture in accordance with the surrounding atmosphere. Its moisture content should therefore be known, as otherwise there may be considerable movement owing to expansion or shrinkage, this depending upon the position in which the wood will be used eventually. It is thus clear that the content should vary in accordance with the use to which the timber will be put.

Moisture content is the weight of moisture expressed as a percentage of the dry weight of the timber. As an example in a piece of wood having, say, 20 per cent. moisture content there is 1 lb. of water for every 5 lb. of dry wood.

Wood pests

There are two ways of measuring the content; by using an electrical instrument which measures the electrical resistance; and by weighing a sample, drying it in an oven, and weighing again. The former calls for an expensive instrument; weighing is relatively simple. In this a small piece is sawn off the board and weighed. Assume that the sample weighs 8 oz. This is termed the "initial weight." It is then placed in an oven and dried at a temperature equivalent to boiling point until there is no further loss of weight. Assume then that when put on the scale for the "dry weight" it is 7 oz. — a difference of 1 oz. The moisture content is thus one-seventh of the dry weight, that is, 14·3 per cent.

The sample should be cut 200 mm. or more from the end of the board as the ends are often drier than the rest. The chart opposite shows the moisture content of timber for various purposes.

Wood pests

Furniture beetle or woodworm. Once the presence of the woodworm has been detected treatment should be begun at once. Affected wood may be half eaten away by the pest or it may show nothing more than one or two holes about 1·5 mm. in diameter, but the insidious nature of the trouble is that the interior may be in a very bad state leaving a surface shell of sound wood. The holes are the points from which the beetle emerges, not the point of entry.

The cycle of events is this. The beetles may be introduced in other furniture or they may enter through an open window, since they live in a natural state in the dead branches of trees. They are very small and the average man would probably not connect them with woodworm. The female beetle lays her eggs in crevices in the wood, then dies. Small white grubs hatch out from the eggs and begin to burrow into the wood. They work on in this way for perhaps a year or two years leaving behind them in the tunnel a light, fine powder. Finally the grub drives a tunnel towards the surface of the wood where it bores a chamber in which it lies up and turns into a chrysalis. After a few weeks it develops into a beetle with wings, legs, and so on, and bites its way through to the surface and emerges. The male and female beetles mate and the whole thing starts again. It is during June, July, and August that this exodus takes place, though it may be as early as May.

The most usual treatment is the application of a proprietary insecticide made specially for the purpose. The powder should be removed from the holes as far as possible to enable the liquid to penetrate. A pricker can be used or a vacuum cleaner is sometimes useful. The liquid is fed into the holes with a small brush or a fountain pen filler. If the area is large the liquid will have to be brushed in.

One treatment may not effect a cure, since individual beetles may escape. A watch should therefore be kept on the furniture. A good plan is to lightly ring treated holes so that fresh ones may be recognised. When treating the wood rub the insecticide into all crevices whether near the holes or not.

Another method of treatment, which, however, involves sending the infected furniture to a firm with the necessary equipment, is that of fumigation. The furniture is placed in a special chamber, which is then filled with a poisonous gas.

When examining old furniture in which the beetle is suspected, look out for a light fine powder which may lie on the surface or have dropped to the floor.

Death-watch beetle. This pest is larger than the furniture beetle and generally attacks large pieces of timber – roofs, beams, and so on. The beetles emerge in April, May, and June, and lay their eggs in crevices or old exit holes. After hatching out the grub burrows into the wood for two years or so, then changes into a chrysalis, and eventually bores its way out to begin another cycle of events. The holes are about 3·0 mm. diameter. As the beetles are able to fly the pest can spread easily to all parts of the building.

Moisture Contents of Timber for Various Purposes

THE FIGURES FOR DIFFERENT SPECIES VARY, AND THE CHART SHOWS ONLY AVERAGE VALUES

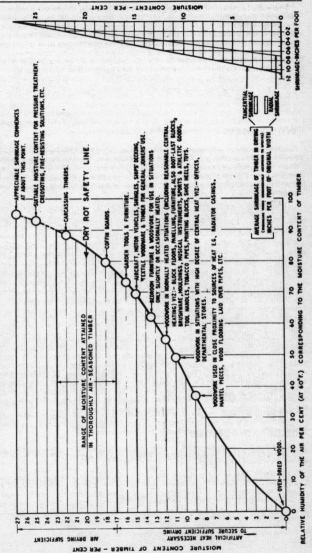

MOISTURE CONTENT — PER CENT

SHRINKAGE-INCHES PER FOOT

TANGENTIAL SHRINKAGE

RADIAL SHRINKAGE

AVERAGE SHRINKAGE OF TIMBER IN DRYING
INCHES PER FOOT OF ORIGINAL WIDTH

APPRECIABLE SHRINKAGE COMMENCES AT ABOUT THIS POINT.

SUITABLE MOISTURE CONTENT FOR PRESSURE TREATMENT, CREOSOTING, FIRE-RESISTING SOLUTIONS, ETC.

CARCASSING TIMBERS.

DRY ROT SAFETY LINE.

COFFIN BOARDS.

GARDEN TOOLS & FURNITURE.

AIRCRAFT, MOTOR VEHICLES, SHINGLES, SHIPS' DECKING, TEXTILE WOODWARE & TIMBER FOR GENERAL JOINERS' USE.

BEDROOM FURNITURE & WOODWORK FOR USE IN SITUATIONS ONLY SLIGHTLY OR OCCASIONALLY HEATED.

WOODWORK IN NORMALLY HEATED SITUATIONS (INCLUDING REASONABLE CENTRAL HEATING) VIZ:— BLOCK FLOORS, PANELLING, FURNITURE, ALSO ROOT-LAST BLOCKS, BRUSHWARE, MOULDINGS, MUSICAL INSTRUMENTS, SPORTS & ATHLETIC GOODS, TOOL HANDLES, TOBACCO PIPES, PRINTING BLOCKS, SHOE HEELS, TOYS.

WOODWORK IN SITUATIONS WITH HIGH DEGREE OF CENTRAL HEAT VIZ:— OFFICES, DEPARTMENTAL STORES.

WOODWORK USED IN CLOSE PROXIMITY TO SOURCES OF HEAT E.G., RADIATOR CASINGS.

WOODWORK IN CLOSE PROXIMITY TO SOURCES OF HEAT E.G., MANTEL PIECES, WOOD FLOORING LAID OVER PIPES, ETC.

OVEN-DRIED WOOD.

RANGE OF MOISTURE CONTENT ATTAINED IN THOROUGHLY AIR-SEASONED TIMBER

AIR DRYING SUFFICIENT

ARTIFICIAL HEAT NECESSARY TO SECURE SUFFICIENT DRYING

MOISTURE CONTENT OF TIMBER — PER CENT

RELATIVE HUMIDITY OF THE AIR PER CENT (AT 60°F.) CORRESPONDING TO THE MOISTURE CONTENT OF TIMBER

Moisture content

All dust and really rotten wood should be removed and the whole given a thorough treatment with a special insecticide. If necessary, any paint or varnish should be scraped off to help penetration, and in some cases it is an advantage to bore holes into which the liquid can be poured, enabling it to reach otherwise inaccessible parts. When it is feasible to take joints apart it is an advantage to do so to enable the inner surface to be reached.

Dry rot. This term is somewhat misleading, for, although the wood after attack has a cracked and dry appearance, the trouble always occurs in a damp, badly ventilated position. It is caused by a fungus which feeds upon the timber, gradually eating away the fibres and producing a sort of cubical, cracked effect. The fungus itself is a white growth, often with patches of yellow, and it sends out lace-like strands to attack sound timber in the locality. Timber with a moisture content of less than 20 per cent. is seldom attacked. Floors are subject to dry rot when there is an absence of air bricks beneath or if the latter have become stopped up. Trouble may also be due to the lack of honeycomb openings in sleeper walls. The lack of a dampcourse is also a possible cause.

The commonest of the fungi is the *Merulius lacrymans*. It thrives chiefly upon the sapwood of softwoods, but will also attack the heartwood. Hardwoods too are subject to it, though to a lesser extent. It can be introduced in many ways. The spores can be carried in by the wind, they can be present in a sack of coals or they even penetrate through mortar; and if they lodge on a piece of damp timber and the conditions are right, they begin to germinate.

A second fungus is the *Coniophora cerebella*, which is found often in damp cellars. Very wet timbers are attacked, and it may therefore be suspected in the locality of leaking pipes and other damp positions.

Timber which has the dry rot has an unmistakable appearance, cracks developing both across and with the grain so that the wood looks as though it has been broken up into irregular cubes. In the case of structural timbers there will probably be collapse, as affected wood entirely loses its strength. It is possible, however, for painted woodwork to be affected at the back (where it cannot be seen) leaving a normal appearance at the front. Symptoms of the complaint are an offensive, musty smell, the presence of fine red powder (the spores of the fungus), and surface cracks. Bad warping may also be a sign. Tap the timber to see whether it has a healthy ring or a dead sound. If also a sharp tool such as a bradawl can be pressed in easily, it is a sign of trouble.

Cutting out and burning affected timber is generally the only solution, but before replacing with fresh it is necessary to correct the conditions giving rise to the trouble. This may involve the clearing of air bricks or their introduction if there are not any; the removal of bricks in a sleeper wall to ensure a through draught; and the removal of the causes of damp. Cut away the affected timber well beyond the last sign of rot. Go over all exposed surfaces of both timber and adjoining brickwork with a blowlamp to sterilise it, and give the whole a thorough treatment with a proprietary wood preservative or a good quality creosote. Any new replacement timber must also be thoroughly brushed with a preservative. The old affected timber which has been cut away should be burnt.

Portable machines

A. Electric drill. Various attachments available; circular saw, jigsaw, orbital sander, disc sander, dovetailer, etc.

B. High speed electric router. For working grooves, recesses, mouldings, piercing, etc.

C. Jigsaw. For cutting curves and for internal cuts.

D. Circular saw. For ripping, cross-cutting, etc.

E. Power plane. Used mostly for the rapid reduction of wood.

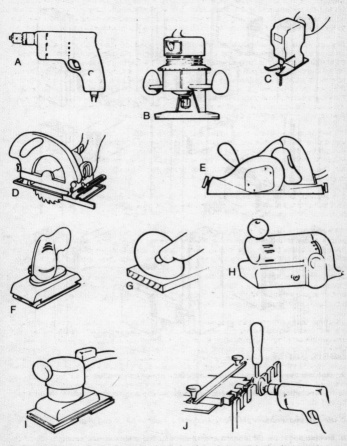

F. Orbital sander. For the final smoothing of surfaces to be polished or lacquered.

G. Flexible disc sander. For the rough cleaning of surfaces.

H. Belt sander. Made in both bench and floor models.

I. Reciprocating sander. With two pads which move towards and away from each other.

J. Dovetailer. An attachment for fitting to an electric drill or router.

Basic joints

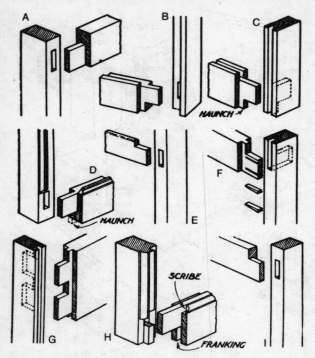

Basic joints

A. Stub mortise and tenon. Door frames, etc. Haunch can be added.

B. Mortise and tenon for rebated frame. Note long and short shoulders. Haunch can be added.

C. Mortise and tenon for grooved framework. Haunch fills in end of groove.

D. Mortise and tenon for rebated and moulded frame. Haunch is optional.

E. Bare-faced mortise and tenon. Tenon is full thickness of rail.

F. Through mortise and tenon. Tenon is wedged at outside.

G. Double mortise and tenon. For wide rails.

H. Mortise and tenon for casement window also for sash window.

I. Bare-faced mortise and tenon. Rail is thinner than upright.

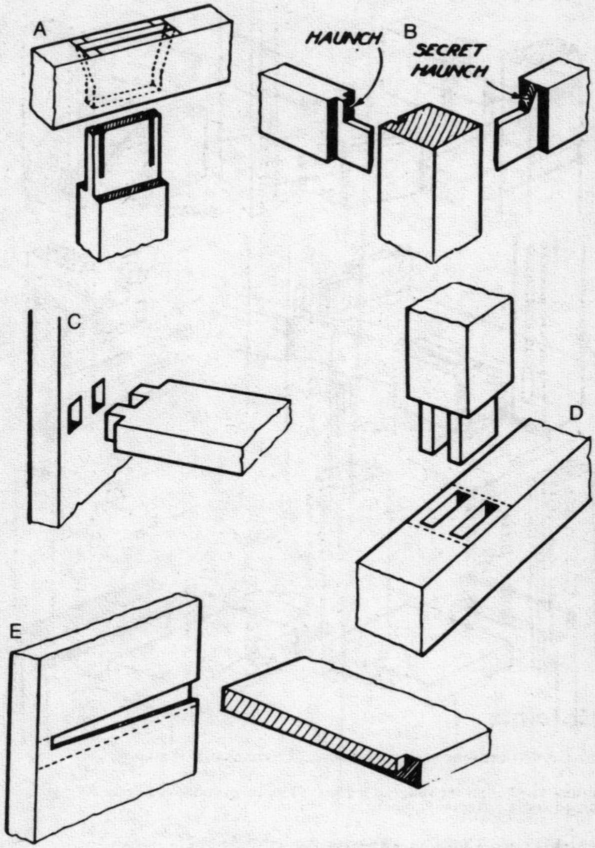

A. Through mortise and tenon. A framing joint.

B. Mortise and tenon for leg and rails. Mortises meet in thickness of wood. Note alternative haunches.

C. Twin tenons for drawer rail.

D. Twin tenons (*right*) **for heavy framing.**

E. Diminished dovetail housing. For shelvings, etc.

Basic joints

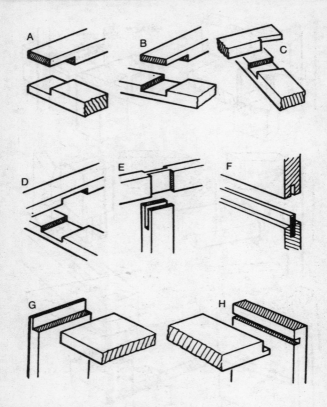

A. **Halved angle.** General framing joint.

B. **Halved T.** Glued together; also screwed when possible.

C. **Dovetail halving.** Glued together; also screwed when possible.

D. **Cross halving.** Framing joint.

E. **Bridle.** General framing.

F. **Loose tongue and groove.** Jointing wide tops, etc.

G. **Simple lap.** Carcase joint. Requires nailing as well as gluing.

92 H. **Bare-faced tongue and groove.** General carcase joint.

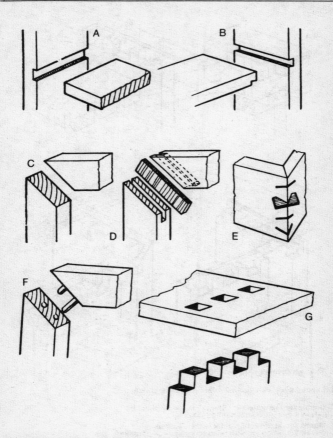

A. Common housing. **B. Bare-faced dovetail housing.** Both used for shelves, partitions, etc. The dovetail is easier to fit if tapered. See page 91.

C. Simple mitre. Frames, mouldings, etc.

D. Tongued mitre. For strengthening plain mitres.

E. Veneer keyed mitre. Used for veneered boxes, etc.

F. Dowelled mitre. Alternative strengthening for plain mitre.

G. Pinning. For carcase partitions, etc.

Basic joints

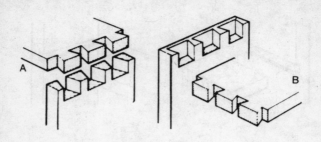

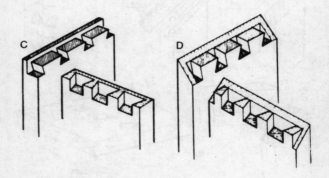

A. Through dovetail. Boxes, carcases, etc.

B. Lapped dovetail. Carcases. Does not show at side.

C. Double lapped dovetail. Shows only end grain of lap.

D. Mitred secret dovetail. Joint entirely hidden.

E. Lapped dovetail for carcase. Rail has fly-piece and is cut around leg and end.

F. Lapped dovetail for carcase. Narrow dovetails prevent corners from curling.

G. Drawer dovetails. Also method of finding slope for dovetails. Some workers prefer dovetails with less slope.

H. Oblique dovetails. For general carcasing, special drawers, etc.

I. Scarf for jointing timber in length. Resists both tension and compression. Extra tenons (dotted lines) help to resist side strain.

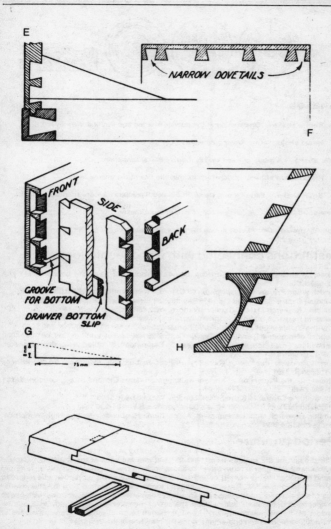

E

NARROW DOVETAILS

F

FRONT

SIDE

BACK

GROOVE FOR BOTTOM

DRAWER BOTTOM SLIP

G

H

75 mm

I

95

Shakes

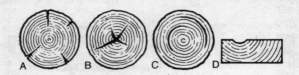

Shakes

A. Radial shake. One starting at the outside of a log and running inwards radially.

B. Heart shake. One running outwards from the pith.

Star shake. A group of heart shakes roughly in star formation.

C. Ring or cup shake. One which follows the line of the annual rings.

D. Shell shake. Part of a ring shake. In a board it results in a loose rounded section.

Compound shake. A combination of two or more shakes.

Felling shake. One caused during the process of felling.

Institutions connected with wood technology

British Standards Institution, British Standards House, 2 Park St., London, W1Y 4AA 01-629 9000
British Wood Preserving Association, 62 Oxford Street, London WIN 9WD 01-580-3185
Building Centre of Scotland Ltd., 425 Sauchiehall Street, Glasgow, C.2 041-332 5911
Building Research Station, Garston, Watford, WD2 7JR Garston (Herts) 74040
Building Research Station (Scottish Laboratory), Thorntonhall, Glasgow 041-644 1171
City and Guilds of London Institute, 76 Portland Place, London W1N 4AA 01-580 3050
Council of Industrial Design, The Design Centre, 28 Haymarket, London, S.W.1 01-839 8000
Council for Small Industries in Rural Areas, 35 Camp Road, Wimbledon Common, London, S.W.19 01-946 5101
Forest Products Research Laboratory, Princes Risborough, Aylesbury, Bucks. Princes Risborough 3101
Society for the Protection of Ancient Buildings, 55 Great Ormond Street, London, W.C.1 01-405 2646
The Building Centre, 26 Store Street, London, W.C.1 01-636 5400
The National Trust, 42 Queen Anne's Gate, London, S.W.1 01-930 1841
Timber Research and Development Association, Hughenden Valley, High Wycombe, Bucks 0240-24 3091

Period furniture

The division of the periods from 1500 to 1800 into the ages of the Carpenter, Cabinet Maker, and Designer is convenient because these terms suggest the type of furniture being produced. In the earliest period furniture was made by the carpenter, who regarded furniture-making as incidental to his general work, and it therefore bore the characteristics of a craftsman used to large joinery work. Soon after 1660 some woodworkers began to specialise in furniture, and so came the age of the cabinet maker. Lastly, at about the middle of the eighteenth century, furniture began to be associated with the names of individual designers and craftsmen, hence the term Age of the Designer.

Period furniture

The age of the carpenter, 1500–1660	Tudor Gothic	1500–1603
	Jacobean	1603–1660
The age of the cabinet maker, 1660–1750	Transitional	1660–1690
	Walnut	1660–1720
	Early Georgian	1714–1750
The age of the designer, 1750–1800	Chippendale	1745–1780
	Adam	1760–1792
	Hepplewhite	1760–1790
	Sheraton	1790–1806
	Regency and George IV	1810–1830
	Victorian	1837–1900

The above dates are approximate only, and are intended to indicate the years when furniture of a certain style was being mainly produced. They do not necessarily show the year in which any of the designers or cabinet makers died.

British monarchs

Henry VII, 1485–1509	(Commonwealth, 1649–1660)	George II, 1727–1760
Henry VIII, 1509–1547	Charles II, 1660–1685	George III, 1760–1820
Edward VI, 1547–1553	James II, 1685–1688	(Regency, 1810–1820)
Mary, 1553–1558	William and Mary, 1689–1702	George IV, 1820–1830
Elizabeth I, 1558–1603	Anne, 1702–1714	William IV, 1830–1837
James I, 1603–1625	George I, 1714–1727	Victoria, 1837–1901
Charles I, 1625–1649		

French monarchs

Francis I, 1515–1547	Henry IV, 1589–1610	Directory, 1795–1799
Henry II, 1547–1559	Louis XIII, 1610–1643	Consulate, 1799–1804
Francis II, 1559–1560	Louis XIV, 1643–1715	Empire (Napoleon I), 1804–1814
Charles IX, 1560–1574	Louis XV, 1715–1774	Louis XVIII, 1814–1824
Henry III, 1574–1589	Louis XVI, 1774–1793	Charles X, 1824–1830
		Louis Philippe, 1830–1848

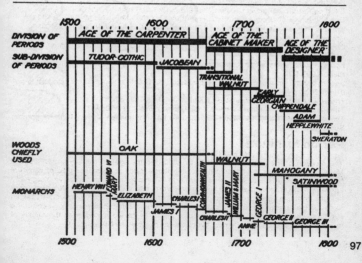

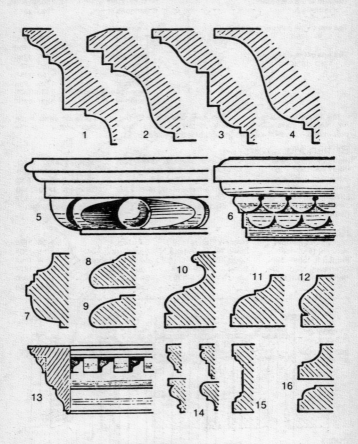

Jacobean period 1603–1660

Jacobean mouldings as applied to furniture were a free and somewhat coarse rendering of the classical.

Nos. 1 to 4 and No. 13 are cornice mouldings.
Nos. 5 to 7 are surbase mouldings.
Nos. 8 and 9 are table or chest top sections.
Nos. 10 to 12, 16 and 17 are suitable for bases.
No. 14 shows panel mouldings and No. 15 a channelling.

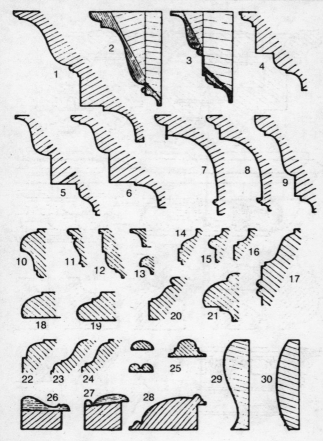

Walnut period 1660–1720

Walnut period mouldings, founded upon the classic, were invariably cross-grained. They were built up of a layer of thin cross-grained walnut upon a pine groundwork. Straight members were often veneered.

Nos. 1 to 9 are cornice mouldings. Nos. 10 to 21 are various table-top and surbase sections. Nos. 22 to 24 are base mouldings. No. 25 shows small beads used for barred doors, drawer edges, etc. Nos. 26 to 28 are mirror-frame sections. Nos. 29 and 30 are frieze contours.

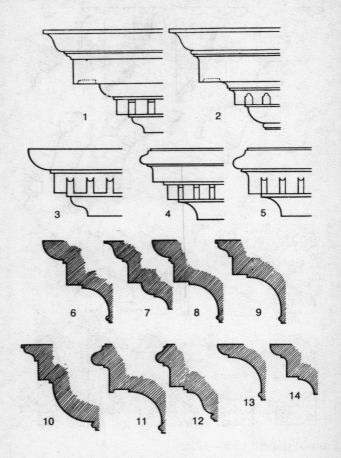

Chippendale period 1745–1780

Mouldings of this period were mostly founded upon classical examples. The sections were frequently carved in the better class work.

Nos. 1 to 14 are cornice mouldings, Nos. 4, 5, 11, and 12 being suitable for a low height level.

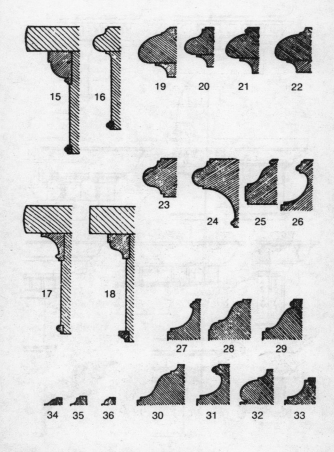

Table sections with frieze rails are given in Nos. 15 to 18.
Nos. 19 to 22 are for tables or low cabinet tops.
Surbase mouldings are shown in Nos. 23 to 26.
Nos. 27 to 33 are base mouldings.
Nos. 34 to 36 are suitable for panels.
The mouldings are taken partly from old furniture and partly from the "Gentleman and Cabinet Maker's Director."

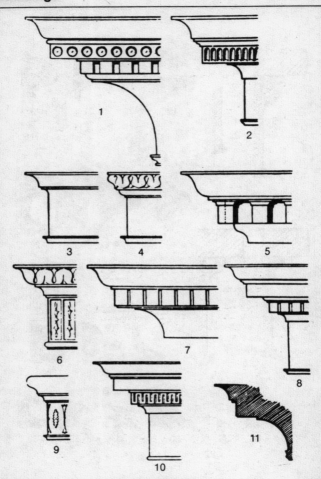

Hepplewhite period 1760–1790

Mouldings of this style were founded upon the classical, but the sections were simplified to make them suitable for the comparatively small size required for furniture. A restrained form of carving was frequently introduced.

Nos. 1 to 13 are cornice mouldings.
Nos. 14 to 20 are surbase sections.
Nos. 21 to 26 are plinth mouldings.

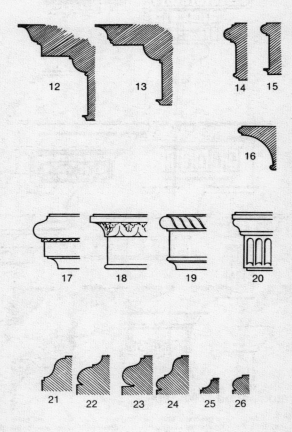

Some Hepplewhite mouldings were decorated with inlay rather than carving. This usually took the form of ebony or satinwood lines or cross-banding. Occasionally the fluted effect shown in 2 was inlaid rather than carved, a recessed appearance being obtained by the use of veneer immersed in hot sand to give a shaded effect.

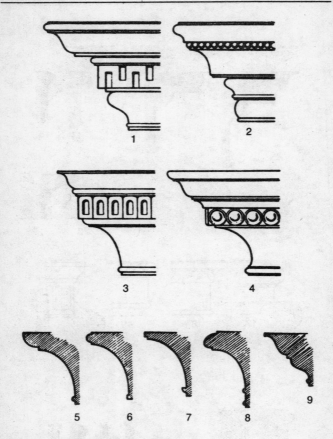

Sheraton period 1790–1806

Sheraton mouldings were generally finer than those of the Chippendale period. Frequently they took the form merely of square fillets, often with inlaid lines or bandings. Larger cornice mouldings were invariably backed with pine for economy.

Nos. 1 to 13 are cornice mouldings. For a low cornice at about eye level Nos. 6, 8, and 12 are specially suitable.

Surbase mouldings are given in Nos. 14 to 17.

Those from 18 to 21 belong to table tops. Sections for bases are Nos. 22 to 25.

Nos. 26 to 28 are barred door mouldings. No. 29 is a shelf mould.

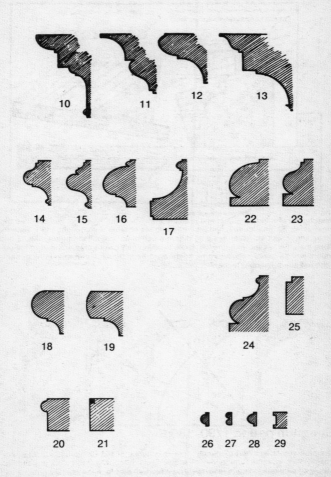

In the case of mouldings decorated with carving the detail was sometimes applied as a strip glued on to a flat surface. Thus the dentil pattern in 1 and the repeat device in 3 was frequently carved separately and added later, though in good quality work it might be carved in the solid.

Useful geometry

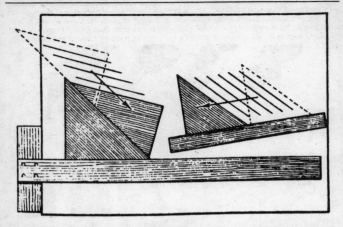

Drawing parallel lines. Horizontal lines are drawn with the T-square. Vertical lines and those at 45, 60, and 30 deg. can be made with set-squares sliding along the T-squares. Other angles can be made by using different combinations of set-squares, sliding one along the other, as shown to the left. Lines at odd angles can be drawn by sliding the set-square along a straight-edge, as given to the right. Keep the square up against the straight-edge and adjust the edge to the required slope.

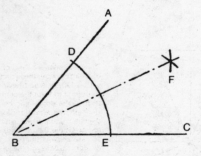

Bisecting an angle. This is often required when mitreing. Some angles are obvious and can be marked with the set-square; 90 deg. and 60 deg. are examples. Odd angles require either the use of a protractor or they must be set out as here. Suppose ABC is the angle to be bisected. Set the compasses to any convenient radius and with centre B draw the arc DE. With centres D and E describe two arcs to cut at F, using the same radius. A line joining F and B bisects the angle ABC.

Development of a conical surface. This is useful in working out the shape of the material for a lampshade or in ascertaining the shape of a sheet of veneer to cover a conical surface. Draw in the elevation of the shape shown by the straight lines ABDC. Project AC and BD to intersect at E. With centre E draw an arc passing through A and B and continuing well to the side.

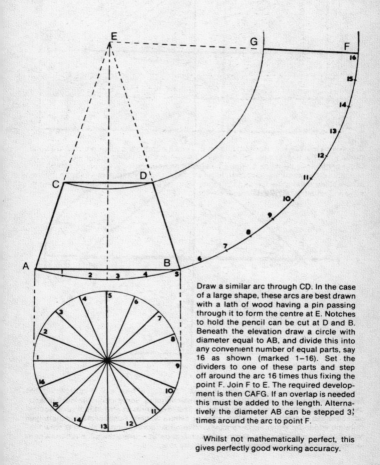

Draw a similar arc through CD. In the case of a large shape, these arcs are best drawn with a lath of wood having a pin passing through it to form the centre at E. Notches to hold the pencil can be cut at D and B. Beneath the elevation draw a circle with diameter equal to AB, and divide this into any convenient number of equal parts, say 16 as shown (marked 1–16). Set the dividers to one of these parts and step off around the arc 16 times thus fixing the point F. Join F to E. The required development is then CAFG. If an overlap is needed this must be added to the length. Alternatively the diameter AB can be stepped 3½ times around the arc to point F.

Whilst not mathematically perfect, this gives perfectly good working accuracy.

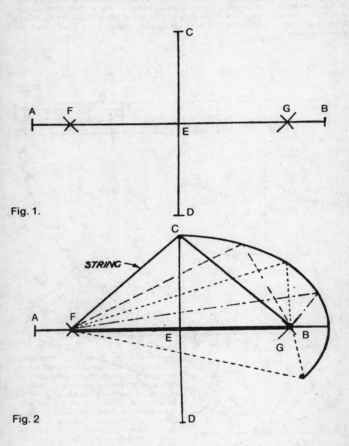

Fig. 1.

Fig. 2

Drawing an ellipse, pin and string method. This is the best way of drawing a large ellipse. Draw in the axes AB, CD, as in Fig. 1. Set a pair of compasses to half AB (that is, AE) and, with centre D, cut AB at F and G. Tap about quarter way in thin panel pins at C, F, and G., and tie a piece of fine string or twine around the pins with a slip knot, thus forming a triangle. Withdraw the pin at C and replace it with a pencil. By moving the pencil along and keeping the string always taut an ellipse is drawn, as in Fig. 2. It is advisable to strain the string first, as otherwise it may become stretched.

108

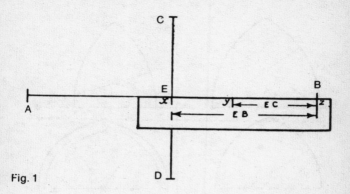

Fig. 1

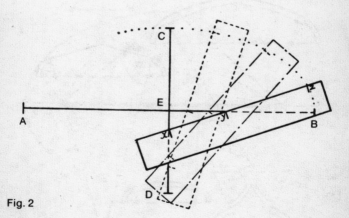

Fig. 2

Drawing an ellipse, trammel method. Although a large ellipse can be drawn by this method, it is more generally useful for small sizes. Draw in the axes AB and CD to intersect at E, as in Fig. 1. Cut a strip of paper or thin card to a straight edge, and mark along the straight edge the distance EB (xz). From z mark in distance EC (y). Now keeping the pencil marks (xy) always up to the lines of both axes make a pencil mark on the paper at z. Gradually move the paper round, making a fresh mark at z. In this way the shape can be plotted in, as in Fig. 2, and it is only a case of joining the dots to make the ellipse

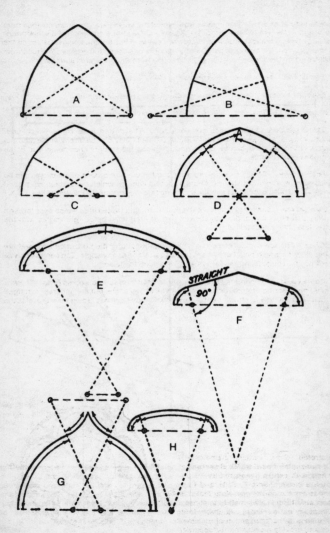

Useful geometry

Arches

How to set out arches. The centres from which the curves are struck are obvious from the diagrams. Where two curves join or where a curve joins a straight line it is important that they flow into each other in an unbroken sweep. They are thus tangential. In all the examples given, the curves which join the uprights or sides of the arches are struck from a centre which lies somewhere along the base line from which the arch springs.

A. Equilateral. The centres are at the spring of the arch.

B. Lancet. Gives a sharply pointed arch. Centres are outside the arch.

C. Drop. Forms a flat arch. Centres are within the arch.

D. Three centred. Arch shapes are compound. The dotted lines along which both centres are placed show where the two curves meet. They can be at any angle, and the centres of the top curve can be in any position along the straight lines below that of the common or lower curve.

E. Four centred. Forms a depressed arch, though the proportions of the curves can be varied to give alternative shapes. Angle of dotted lines on which the centres are placed can be varied; also position of centres providing that they remain on the dotted line.

F. Straight top. Similar to E, but the top part is straight. Dotted lines which pass through centres can be at any angle, but straight part of arch must be at right angles with the dotted line (that is, tangential).

G. Ogee. The lower centres can be in any position along the horizontal line, and the dotted lines on which both centres are placed can slope at any angle. Top centres can be in any position outside the arch which will give a point to the arch.

H. Depressed. Side centres are always at intersection of dotted sloping lines with horizontal line at spring of arch. Dotted lines can be at any angle, but are generally arranged so that centre curve is struck from a very considerably greater radius than those at the sides.

Quatrefoil. Draw vertical diameter AB and horizontal diameter CD. Bisect AE at F, and with centre E and radius FE describe a circle. Points F, G, H, and I are centres for the small arcs. Note that it is usual also to put in diameters at 45 deg. (shown in dotted lines), as these form mitre lines at the intersection of the small arcs and provide a check on the accuracy of the work.

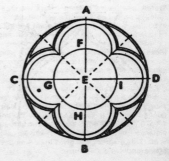

Useful geometry

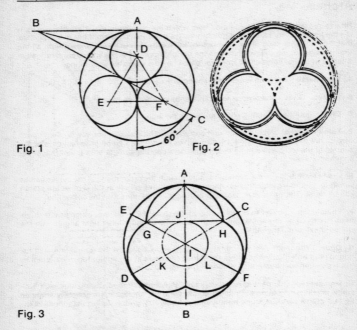

Fig. 1

Fig. 2

Fig. 3

Setting out a trefoil. A detail often found in Gothic work in which three small circles are placed within a large one. Draw in a vertical diameter as in Fig. 1 and at point A draw a tangent AB. Draw in a second diameter BC at 60 deg. with the first, Fig. 1. Bisect the angle ABC and at the point where it cuts the vertical diameter, D, draw in the equilateral triangle DEF. The points of this triangle are the centres of the small circles. The secondary lines of the trefoil are put in as in Fig. 2.

Trefoil, alternative pattern. Here the inner curves are semi-circles, and a more open trefoil is produced. Draw the vertical diameter AB and two other diameters CD and EF all at 60 deg. At point A draw in the right-angled triangle AGH. With centre I and radius IJ draw in a circle. Points J, K, and L are centres for the semi-circles.

Measuring compound sloping lines. When an oblique line slopes away from you it cannot be directly measured in either plan or elevation. You have to throw it flat so that it can be directly measured in plan.

A practical example of this is a hipped roof. Figs. 1 and 2 show elevations and plan, and clearly the hip AC (or BC) cannot be measured because it slopes away from you whichever view you take. The simplest way it to imagine the roof to be cut out in cardboard and opened out flat. In the plan continue the lines AA, BB, and AB. Draw line ab parallel with AB at a distance from C equal to X on side elevation. Also draw line aa parallel with AA at a distance from CC equal to Z on end elevation. Join aC and bC. The true length of the hip is aC. This diagram also gives the development of the roof required when making a cardboard model or dolls' house.

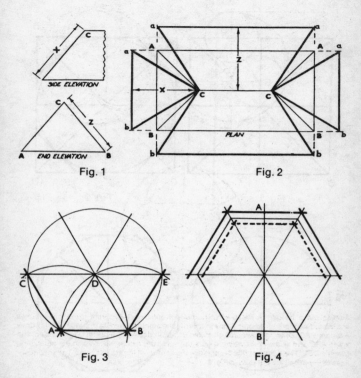

Fig. 1

Fig. 2

Fig. 3

Fig. 4

Drawing a hexagon. There are two ways in which the problem may be presented; the size from point to point, or the size measured over two parallel sides. The simplest way in both cases is to use the T-square and 60 deg. set square since all the inner angles of the figure are 120 deg.

Point-to-point. Draw a horizontal base line (AB) exactly half the point to point size. With radius (AB) and centre first (A) then (B) describe two arcs to intersect at (D) and extend to (C) and (E). Draw a second horizontal line through (D) and put in (AC) and (BE). With radius (DA) and centre (D) draw a circle and complete the hexagon. Fig. 3.

Side-to-side measurement. Draw a hexagon similarly to Fig. 3. Its exact size is not important but its point-to-point size should be somewhere in the region of the side-to-side measurement. Draw a vertical line (AB) through the centre as in Fig. 4. Mark on this the side-to-side required and put in the hexagon sides parallel with the hexagon already drawn. They may be either inside or outside according to the size of the original hexagon. 113

Useful geometry

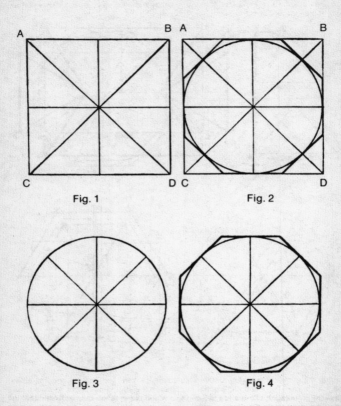

Fig. 1

Fig. 2

Fig. 3

Fig. 4

Drawing an octagon in a square. This is needed when a square of wood has to be planed to form an octagonal section. It enables the width of the chamfers to be ascertained. Assume ABDC in Fig. 1 to be the square. Draw in diagonals and where they intersect draw in upright and horizontal centre lines (Fig. 1). Using the point of intersection as centre draw in a circle with radius equal to half the centre line, and where this cuts the diagonals draw in lines at 45 deg. This produces the octagon, as shown in Fig. 2.

Drawing an octagon outside a circle. For some setting-out work this is often needed. It is similar to the preceding problem. Draw upright and horizontal diameters, and at 45 deg. to these put in two other diameters as in Fig. 3. Where these cut the circle draw in tangents with the 45 deg. set-square as in Fig. 4, thus forming the octagon.

Useful geometry

Drawing an octagon inside a circle. Proceed as in the previous problem, drawing the octagon outside the circle, as in Fig. 1. From the points of the octagon draw in further diagonals as shown by the dotted lines. From where these lines cut the circle draw in the sides of the octagon, as in Fig. 2.

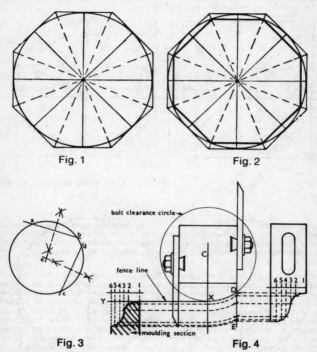

Fig. 1

Fig. 2

Fig. 3

Fig. 4

Finding the centre of a circle. Draw in two chords (*ab*) and (*cd*) roughly at right angles with each other. The exact angle is not important but it should be neither too small nor too large. Bisect each chord and produce the bisecting lines to intersect at (*e*), this being the centre of the circle. Fig. 3.

Cutter projection scale. This is required for slotted collars or the square cutter block of a spindle moulder. Draw in a plàn of the cutter block in full size and put in the bolt-clearance circle. Draw a centre line parallel with the cutters, and at its intersection with the bolt-clearance circle (*X*), draw a fence line (*XY*) at right angles with it. Draw the required moulding section and put in several vertical lines 1–6. Where these intersect the moulding profile draw horizontals to cut the projected centre line (*CX*). Each line is carried in an arc to intersect a line (*DE*) projected from the second cutter face, and carried horizontally to intersect with vertical lines 1–6 drawn on the cutter face to the right and having the same spacing as those of the moulding 'section'. A curve drawn through the points of intersection gives the required cutter profile.

Mitres

A mitre always halves the angle of the joining pieces. Most mouldings join at 90 deg., so that the commonest mitre is at 45 deg. (Fig. 1, A). B and C show the mitres of odd angles. Unless the mitre halves the over-all angle the members will not coincide. D shows the application to the bars of a door. Here it is advisable to work to the centre line of the moulding, all the mitres intersecting on this line.

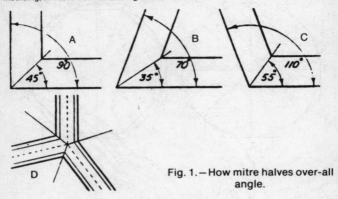

Fig. 1.—How mitre halves over-all angle.

Curved mouldings. When curved and straight mouldings have to be mitred together, one of two things must happen: either a curved mitre must be used or the section of one or other of the mouldings must be altered. Otherwise the members will not coincide. Generally it is better to use a curved mitre, because it is simpler than to alter the section.

An example of a curved mitre is given at A (Fig. 2), and B shows how the curve is obtained: Draw in the straight moulding in full size, putting in all the members. If there is one large section with no small members, put in a series of imaginary lines. Draw in the curved moulding, spacing the members exactly as in the straight part, or giving the imaginary lines exactly the same spacing. A simple way of doing this is to place a piece of paper across the straight part exactly at right angles and mark off the members. Then, placing the paper radially across the curve, transfer the marks, and draw in the curved members. Draw in a line freehand through the intersection of the members, this being the curve of the mitre. The dotted line in B is straight and is put in to make the true mitre obvious.

When two mouldings of the same curvature meet, both curving the same way, the mitre is straight as at C. If one of them is of quicker curvature the mitre is curved (D). Mouldings of the same curvature but curving the opposite way need a curved mitre as at E.

Raking mouldings. These are often used in classical pediments as in overdoors or above the cornice of a bookcase. The section of the raking moulding being fixed, the problem is to obtain the section to which the lower and top end moulds have to be worked. Draw in the raking moulding and at right angles to it put in the section as shown at A, Fig. 3. Make a series of arbitrary lines parallel with slope of the moulding, these cutting the section at a–h. From the points of intersection draw a series of lines at right angles with the slope up to the top. From the point X draw a horizontal line, and to it transfer with compasses the lines drawn across the moulding, using X as centre. Drop vertical lines down from the horizontal line and the intersections with the arbitrary lines form points in the required section. B shows the finished section. The shape of the top mould can be put in similarly. Instead of using compasses the thickness of the moulding at the various points a–h could be marked off on the edge of a piece of paper and transferred to the end.

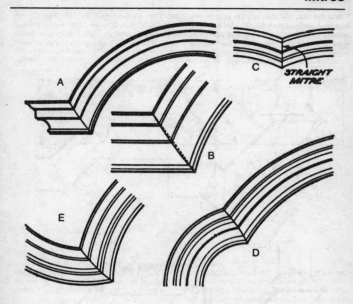

Fig. 2. — Mitres for curved and straight mouldings.

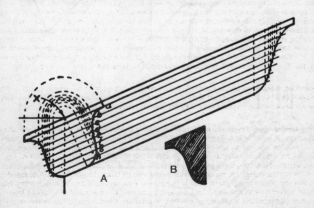

Fig. 3. — Raking mould. Ascertaining section of return.   117

Mitres

Small breaks. Complications sometimes arise when a wide moulding has to be mitred around a surface with small internal breaks. What happens is that the mitre lines intersect before the full width of the moulding is reached. Draw in the full width of the moulding and mark in the first mitres as at A, halving the over-all angles. From the point of intersection draw in second mitres to the point where the lines showing the moulding width cut as shown at B. This second mitre halves the new angle. C shows the completed moulding.

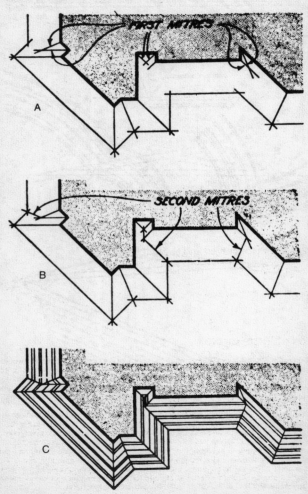

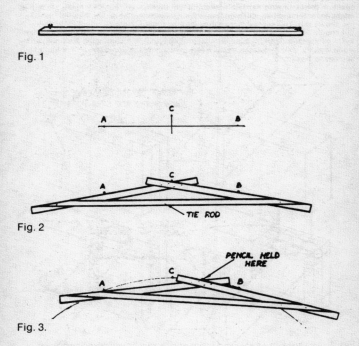

Fig. 1

Fig. 2

TIE ROD

PENCIL HELD
HERE

Fig. 3.

Arcs of large circles

Radius rod. When it is possible to reach the centre of the circle an arc can be struck with a radius rod, this consisting of a wood batten with a nail driven in at one end to act as centre, and a notch at the other to hold a pencil. Sometimes it is more convenient to put notches in the edge of the lath rather than the end. A whole number of concentric circles can be drawn in this way without shifting the nail on which the rod is centred. Fig. 1.

Sliding frame. If it is not possible to reach the centre of the circle the method above can be used. The required arc has to pass through points A, C, and B, shown in Fig. 2. Drive in nails at all three points and prepare two laths with straight edges. Rest one against AC and the other against CB, the two forming a notch at the top. Nail the two together and fix a tie rod to make the whole rigid, as in Fig. 3. Withdraw the nail at C and substitute a pencil. Slide the frame sideways, keeping the edges always against the nails at A and B. Fig. 3. This enables a true arc to be drawn, the length of which is bounded only by the length of the laths. If the arc is short of what is required further nails can be knocked in on the arc already drawn in.

119

Perspective sketching

To be able to sketch in perspective is of great help in woodwork. Those sitting for examinations are often called upon to make small thumbnail sketches to explain points of detail; and the man making an item of woodwork will find it invaluable to sketch perspective details of involved joints, because the sketch will frequently reveal faults that might not otherwise have been discovered. If a joint cannot be drawn, it cannot be made.

It should be realised that these notes do not pretend to explain the full system of drawing in perspective. Their purpose is to suggest ways in which convincing drawings can be made quickly, either to make detail clear, to to show the appearance of a thing as it appears to the eye.

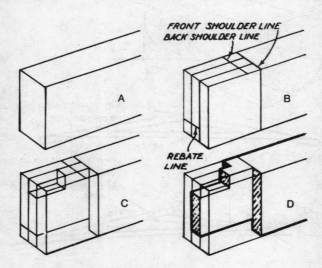

Fig. 1. — Stages in sketching long-and-short shouldered tenon.

Taking first sketches such as joints, the rule is to make the drawing in the order in which you would do the actual work. Fig. 1 shows the stages in drawing a haunched tenon joint with long-and-short shoulders for a rebated frame. The squared end of the wood is sketched in lightly as at (A), as near as possible to the correct proportions. On it are drawn the shoulder lines as at (B), also the gauge marks of the tenon. The gauge lines showing the rebate cannot be seen in this view, but one can be put in at the end. This is important because the rebating removes part of the tenon, and this must be allowed for. (C) shows the final preliminary marking in which the haunch is drawn in.

Now lightly dust down the whole drawing with the rubber and proceed to put in firmly the actual lines of the joint. If the construction lines remain lightly they will do no harm. All edges *across* which you look should be bold and black. Inner lines are lighter yet firm, and end grain hatching is put in free hand with a light touch. The effect is shown at (D) from which the form of the joint is obvious.

Before beginning such a drawing it is as well to roughly sketch it on scrap paper because it often happens that a different view point will give a clearer idea of the joint. This is especially the case where mitres are involved, because these often have the trick of running straight forward so that no surface can be shown. By twisting the wood slightly it can often be made to show the surface of the mitre without adversely affecting other parts of the joint.

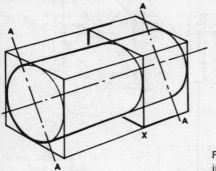

Fig. 2. — Drawing cylinder in perspective.

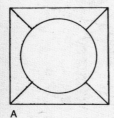

Fig. 3. — Built-up pattern with centre circle to be sketched in perspective.

Now suppose a cylinder has to be shown in perspective. The end will appear as an ellipse, but in what direction do the axes run? Put in an imaginary line to run through the middle of the rod and draw lines at right angles, as at (A–A), Fig. 2. These become the major axes, and the ellipses can be drawn about these as shown. The outer lines of the rod converge towards the rear, of course (equally each side of the centre line), but this only means that the ellipse at the far end is smaller. The lines of the axes are at the same angle.

The question of the width of the ellipse arises, and it is a great help in judging this width if the whole thing is imagined as being in a square of wood, as shown by the light lines. It is far easier to judge the truth of a square shown in perspective, and if you fit the ellipse into this it will invariably look right. In some cases, of course, both square and cylinder are needed, and the way in which the sides are tangential to the ellipse is obvious at (X). Connected with the above but dealt with in a different way is the panel at (A), Fig. 3. It represents a built-up veneer pattern with centre circle such as might appear on a cabinet front. It has to be shown in perspective as at (B). Here the simplest way is to draw in lightly the lines marking the extent of the circle (xx and yy), add the diagonals, and where these intersect put in centre lines. The ellipse can then be put in, remembering that the lines xx and yy will be tangential to the curve at the points of intersection with the centre lines (C). 121

Perspective sketching

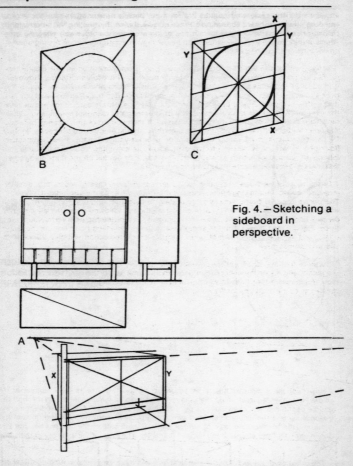

Fig. 4. – Sketching a
sideboard in
perspective.

To make a perspective sketch of a piece of furniture, it is necessary to start off with elevations. Apart from the latter giving correct proportions it enables exact heights to be measured off on to the perspective. Have as long a drawing board as possible and pin the paper to one end (the left is generally the more convenient). Lightly rough in how you want the perspective to look, remembering that a low view point always adds dignity. This means that you see only a minimum of top in sideboards and tables, and only a little of the seat of a chair.

Draw a vertical line to represent the near corner of the item, and transfer all the various heights from the elevations on to it, as in Fig. 4. The sideboard is in the region of 3 ft. high, and the view point might be about 3 ft. 6 in. high. Draw a horizontal line at this height, extending on to the board at each side. Pins are tapped in on this line to give the vanishing points (A) and (B), one being fairly close to the drawing and the other well away. All lines which are horizontal in the elevations can be put in with the straight-edge resting against one or other of these pins as shown.

Actual heights are transferred to the drawing as already mentioned, but clearly this cannot be done with horizontal measurements because of the foreshortening. However, it is possible to estimate them closely. Sketch in what looks about right, putting in the over-all floor plan, as this is always a good guide. Now turn to the elevations and put in a plan of the over-all size and draw a diagonal, as in Fig. 4. Now clearly in the perspective the over-all width of the drawing cannot be greater than this diagonal length, and will, in fact, be a trifle less owing to the foreshortening. If then you make the distance between the outer verticals (X) and (Y) a little less than the diagonal length, you cannot be far out. Of course, it does to an extent depend upon how far your estimate of the perspective floor plan is correct in relation to the plan below the elevation. You have to judge the relative proportion of length to depth, and it is easier to do this on the floor plan rather than the top because you are looking down on it more.

Suppose now the sideboard has a centre vertical division. Clearly you cannot directly measure this on the drawing because the near portion will appear wider since it is nearer. The centre is easily found, however, by putting in diagonals and drawing a vertical line where these intersect, as in Fig. 5. A similar method is followed when the elevation is divided into three equal parts. Draw the diagonals, and divide the near *vertical* line into three, Fig. 6. Lines drawn with the straight-edge to the vanishing point will cut the diagonals, and vertical lines drawn through the points of intersection will give the correct subdivision into three.

Suppose that the centre portion is wider than the other two, as in Fig. 7. Again draw the diagonals, and divide the near upright line into the same proportions as those required in plan. Put in converging lines to the vanishing point and add diagonals. The intersection of the two gives the positions for the uprights.

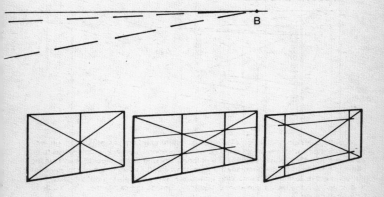

Fig. 5. — Dividing into two lengthwise.

Fig. 6. — Dividing into three lengthwise.

Fig. 7. — Unequal divisions in length.

Scales

Scales are a convenient means of presenting in a small drawing the proportions and sizes of a large object. Furthermore a scale enables a full-sizing of the scale drawing to be made subsequently without reference to the object itself.

In a scale a small measurement represents a larger one in the object itself. For instance, in a '100 mm. to the metre' scale every 100 mm. in the scale represents 1 metre on the

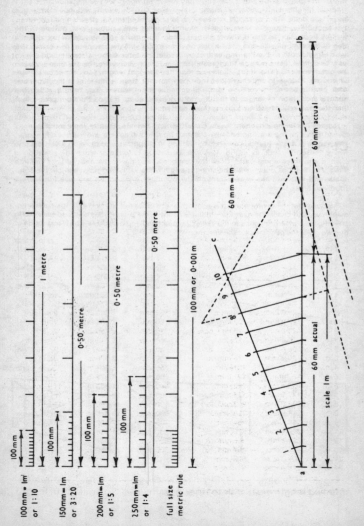

object; 50 mm. represents 0·5 m., and so on. The larger the scale the more accurate the drawing is likely to be but of course it takes a larger sheet of paper and the scale is usually chosen as a matter of convenience. For furniture a scale of 150 mm. = 1 metre (or $\frac{3}{20}$) is generally convenient. For a smaller drawing it could be 100 mm. = 1 metre (or $\frac{1}{10}$); for a larger one 200 mm. = 1 metre (or $\frac{1}{5}$). Four scales are given on page 124 but it is a simple matter to make a scale and it can be to any desired proportion. For instance, in Fig. 1 is the method of making a scale of 60 mm. = 1 metre. Generally there is no special advantage in an odd scale such as this, but it is given to show the method. Draw a line (ab) of any convenient length and make a mark along it at every 60 mm., either marking directly from a metric rule or stepping out with dividers. From (a) draw a second line (ac) at about 30 deg. with (ab), and, starting from (a), step off 10 spaces using dividers. The distance to which the dividers is set is not important, though the total distance stepped should not vary too widely from the scale size (60 mm.). Hold the T-square free on the board, place a set-square upon it and adjust the two so that the 'upright' edge of the set-square aligns with mark 10 on (ac) and the first 60 mm. mark on (ab). Draw a line joining the two marks and, holding the T-square firm, slide the set-square to the next mark (no. 9) and draw a second line parallel with the first. Repeat the process at no. 8 and so on to mark no. 1. At the points on (ab) where the sloping lines intersect, draw short lines square with (ab). Each division represents 0·1 m. or 100 mm. These can be subdivided to show 10 mm. scale sizes, but it is impracticable to subdivide further into 1 mm. sizes in so small a scale.

Conversion tables

Imperial	Metric	Woodworker's Parlance	Metric	Imperial	Woodworker's Parlance
$\frac{1}{32}$ in.	0·8 mm.	1 mm. bare	1 mm.	0·039 in.	$\frac{1}{16}$ in. bare
$\frac{1}{16}$ in.	1·6 mm.	1½ mm.	2 mm.	0·078 in.	$\frac{1}{16}$ in. full
$\frac{1}{8}$ in.	3·2 mm.	3 mm. full	3 mm.	0·118 in.	$\frac{1}{8}$ in. bare
$\frac{3}{16}$ in.	4·8 mm.	5 mm. bare	4 mm.	0·157 in.	$\frac{3}{16}$ in. full
$\frac{1}{4}$ in.	6·4 mm.	6½ mm.	5 mm.	0·196 in.	$\frac{3}{16}$ in. full
$\frac{5}{16}$ in.	7·9 mm.	8 mm. bare	6 mm.	0·236 in.	$\frac{1}{4}$ in. bare
$\frac{3}{8}$ in.	9·5 mm.	9½ mm.	7 mm.	0·275 in.	$\frac{1}{4}$ in. full
$\frac{7}{16}$ in.	11·1 mm.	11 mm. full	8 mm.	0·314 in.	$\frac{5}{16}$ in.
$\frac{1}{2}$ in.	12·7 mm.	12½ mm. full	9 mm.	0·354 in.	$\frac{3}{8}$ in. bare
$\frac{9}{16}$ in.	14·3 mm.	14½ mm. bare	10 mm.	0·393 in.	$\frac{3}{8}$ in. full
$\frac{5}{8}$ in.	15·9 mm.	16 mm. bare	20 mm.	0·787 in.	$\frac{13}{16}$ in. bare
$\frac{11}{16}$ in.	17·5 mm.	17½ mm.	30 mm.	1·181 in.	1$\frac{3}{16}$ in.
$\frac{3}{4}$ in.	19·1 mm.	19 mm. full	40 mm.	1·574 in.	1$\frac{9}{16}$ in. full
$\frac{13}{16}$ in.	20·6 mm.	20½ mm.	50 mm.	1·968 in.	2 in. bare
$\frac{7}{8}$ in.	22·2 mm.	22 mm. full	60 mm.	2·362 in.	2$\frac{3}{8}$ in. bare
$\frac{15}{16}$ in.	23·8 mm.	24 mm. bare	70 mm.	2·755 in.	2¾ in.
*1 in.	25·4 mm.	25½ mm.	80 mm.	3·148 in.	3$\frac{1}{8}$ in. full
2 in.	50·8 mm.	51 mm. bare	90 mm.	3·542 in.	3$\frac{9}{16}$ in. bare
3 in.	76·2 mm.	76 mm. full	100 mm.	3·936 in.	3$\frac{15}{16}$ in.
4 in.	101·6 mm.	101½ mm.	150 mm.	5·904 in.	5$\frac{15}{16}$ in. bare
5 in.	127 mm.	127 mm.	200 mm.	7·872 in.	7$\frac{7}{8}$ in.
6 in.	152·4 mm.	152½ mm.	300 mm.	11·808 in.	11$\frac{13}{16}$ in.
7 in.	177·8 mm.	178 mm. bare	400 mm.	15·744 in.	15¾ in.
8 in.	203·2 mm.	203 mm. full	500 mm.	19·680 in.	19$\frac{11}{16}$ in.
9 in.	228·6 mm.	228½ mm.	600 mm.	23·616 in.	23$\frac{5}{8}$ in. bare
10 in.	254 mm.	254 mm.	700 mm.	27·552 in.	27$\frac{9}{16}$ in.
11 in.	279·4 mm.	279½ mm.	800 mm.	31·488 in.	31½ in.
12 in.	304·8 mm.	305 mm. bare	900 mm.	35·424 in.	35$\frac{7}{16}$ in.
18 in.	457·2 mm.	457 mm. full	1,000 mm.	39·360 in.	39$\frac{3}{8}$ in. bare
24 in.	609·6 mm.	609½ mm.			
36 in.	914·4 mm.	914½ mm.			

*In the trade all sizes are based on 1 in. = 25 mm.

Index